The Complete Rock & Pop Guitar Player Book 2

WISE PUBLICATIONS
London / New York / Paris / Sydney / Copenhagen / Berlin / Madrid / Tokyo

Exclusive Distributors:
Music Sales Limited, 14/15 Berners Street,
London W1T 3LJ, Great Britain.

Order No. AM952985
ISBN: 0-7119-8185-X

Written and arranged by Rikky Rooksby.
Music Processed by Paul Ewers.
Edited by Sorcha Armstrong.

Cover & book design by Fresh Lemon.
Cover photograph (guitar) by George Taylor.
Artist photographs courtesy of
London Features International/ Redferns.

CD mastered by Jonas Persson.
Guitars by Arthur Dick.
Programming by John Moores and Chris Norton.

Printed in the United Kingdom.

The Complete Rock & Pop Guitar Player
Book 2

INTRODUCTION

This is the second book in *The Complete Rock & Pop Guitar Player* series. As before, all the songs you will learn to play have been big hits for well-known artists.

By following strum patterns in **Book 1** you will already be accustomed to learning songs in this format. **Book 2** features more strumming patterns and some new chords. But it has an extra feature. Some of the songs have short musical examples written in standard notation and guitar-friendly TAB. A fretboard diagram showing the location of all the notes is included.

Full lyrics are included at the back of the book.
The songs have been graded; each one introduces new chords, strum patterns or necessary revision of what you have already learnt.

As with all the books in this course, it is suitable for use with or without a teacher. All the musical examples are recorded for you on the CD, first with the simple guitar strum, and then without as a backing track for you to play along with.

BLUE SUEDE SHOES

Words & Music by Carl Lee Perkins

A9 Chord

X O

Frets

3rd

1

4th

2 3 4

5th

6th

D9 Chord

X

Frets

3rd

1

4th

2 3 3 3

5th

6th

Elvis Presley

'Blue Suede Shoes' was an early hit for Elvis in 1956. It's another example of a rock'n'roll 12-bar but with some new chord substitutions. In Book 1 you saw how a 12-bar could be played with A, D, and E.

You also learned the shapes for **D7** and **E7** which can be substituted for the simple **D** or **E major** to add a bit more 'colour'. The next step is to try the ninth chord.

These five note chords are extensions of sevenths like **D7**, **C7**, **B7**, and are often heard in rock'n'roll and blues music. To get **E9** simply move the **D9** shape up **two frets**.

Notice how on the intro you only strum intermittently in the places indicated. The steady strum does not begin until the **D9** and even so it has more 'spaces' in it than some of the songs you have learned.

Before you start, make sure that you're in tune with our CD. Tuning notes for each string are supplied on **Track 1**.

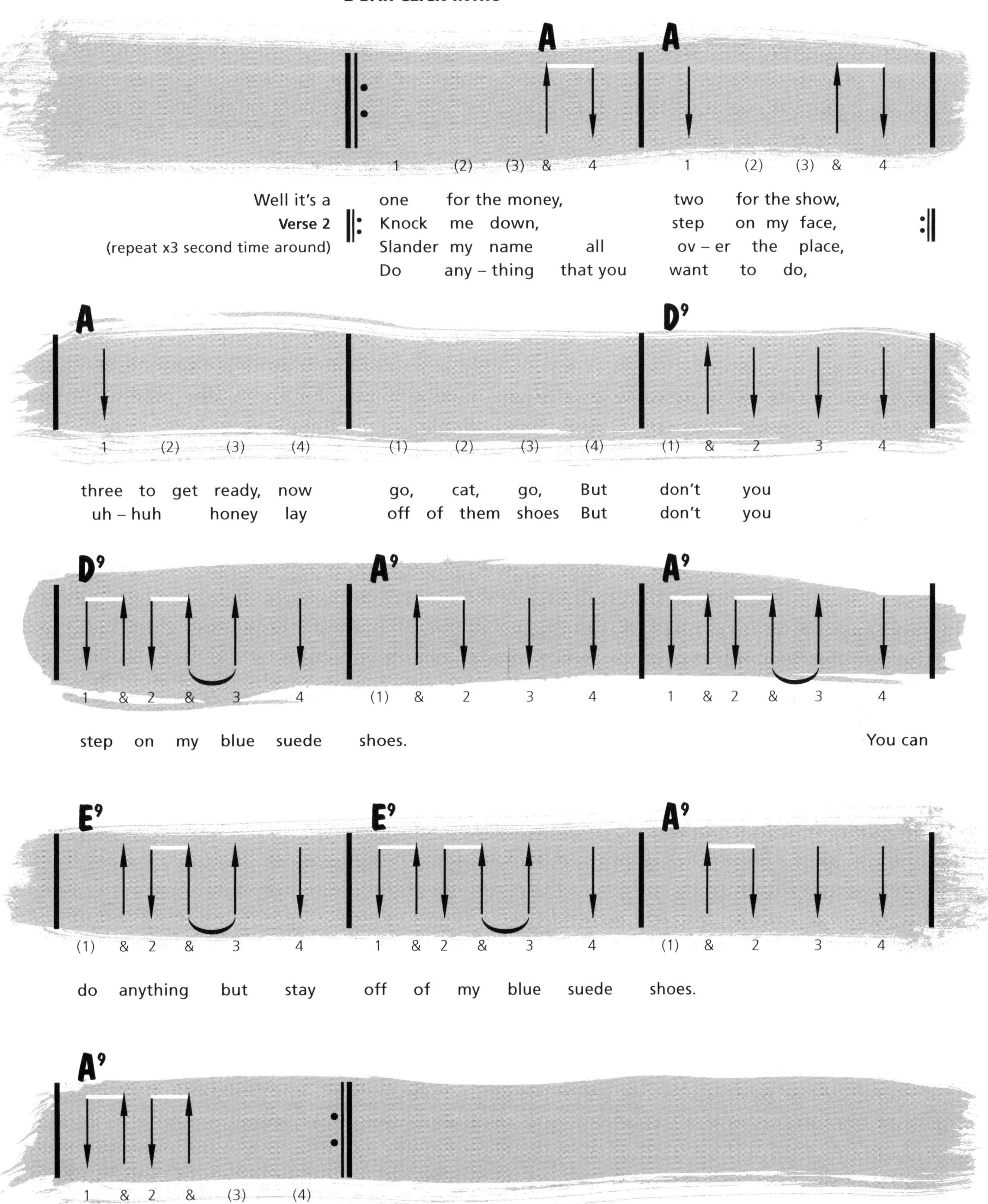
2 BAR CLICK INTRO
A A
1 (2) (3) & 4 1 (2) (3) & 4
Well it's a one for the money, two for the show,
Verse 2 Knock me down, step on my face,
(repeat x3 second time around) Slander my name all ov – er the place,
Do any – thing that you want to do,
A D9
1 (2) (3) (4) (1) (2) (3) (4) (1) & 2 3 4
three to get ready, now go, cat, go, But don't you
uh – huh honey lay off of them shoes But don't you
D9 A9 A9
1 & 2 & 3 4 (1) & 2 3 4 1 & 2 & 3 4
step on my blue suede shoes. You can
E9 E9 A9
(1) & 2 & 3 4 1 & 2 & 3 4 (1) & 2 3 4
do anything but stay off of my blue suede shoes.
A9
1 & 2 & (3) (4)
2. Well you can

DRIFTWOOD

Words & Music by Fran Healy

Fran Healy (Travis)

This ambient ballad by Travis gets part of its sound from the fact that the acoustic guitar on the original is played with a capo at the 7th fret. So to play along with the CD backing track you will need to do the same.

This song requires two new chords: **Asus4** and **G6** - both easy shapes!

In the **Asus4** chord one of the original three notes of **A major** has been replaced by another, the fourth of the scale. '**Sus**' is short for '**suspended**'. You can find out more about the way chords are made in Book 3. For the moment all you need to know is that this **Asus4** is neither major nor minor. Notice it has a tense quality.

Asus4 Chord

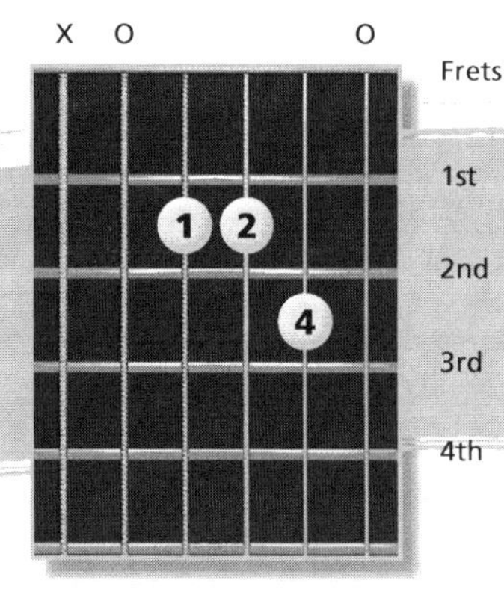

G6 Chord

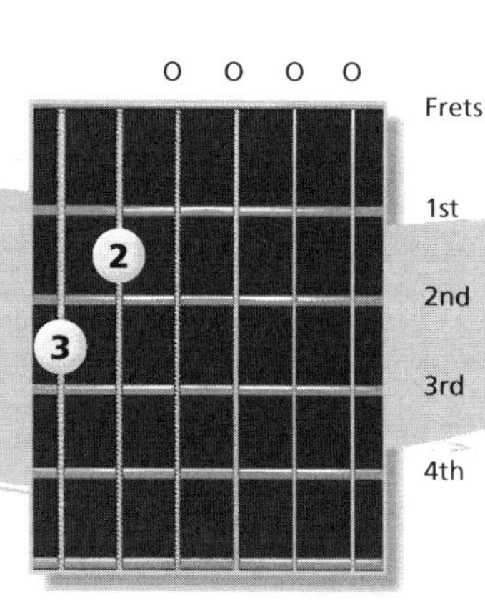

For the chorus of '**Driftwood**' you can try a continuous 16th note strum. This means going down and up twice on each beat, instead of once for 8ths. It is more usual to find 16ths used occasionally because they get quite tiring to play, and also because they only really work at slow to medium speeds. If you wish, you can play 16ths throughout the whole song. To improve the sound of a 16th note strum use a thin pick and brush the strings lightly up and down.

2 BAR CLICK + 4 BAR INTRO

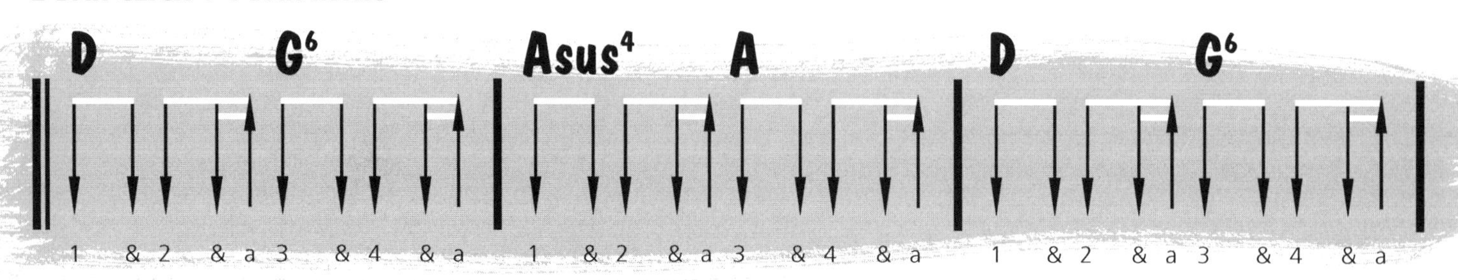

Ev - ery thing is op - en, nothing is set in stone. Rivers turn to oceans,

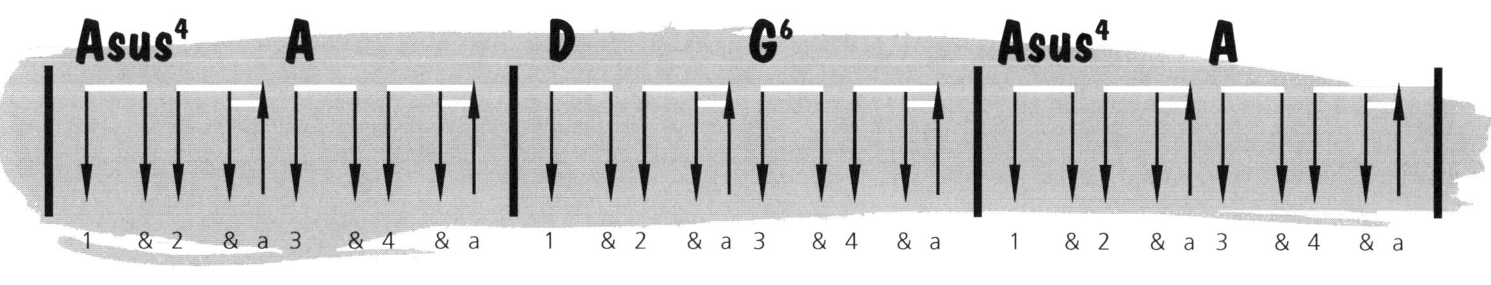

oceans tide you home. Home is where the heart is, but your heart had to roam.

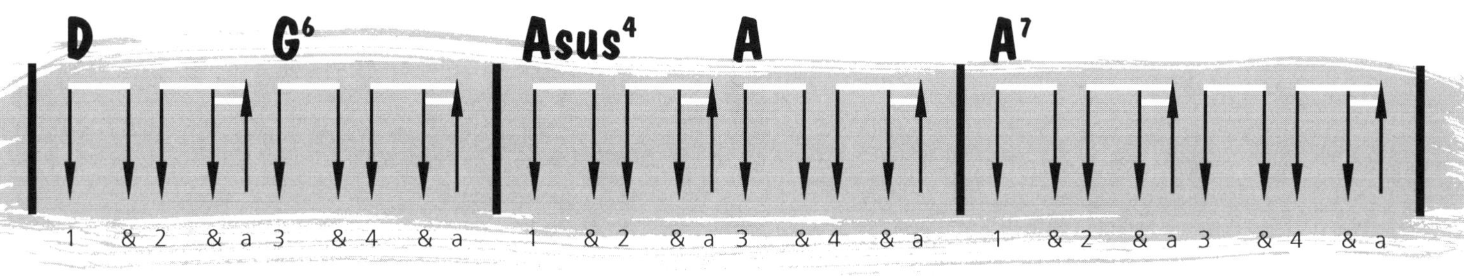

Drifting ov - er bridges ne - ver to re - turn, watch - ing bridges burn. You're

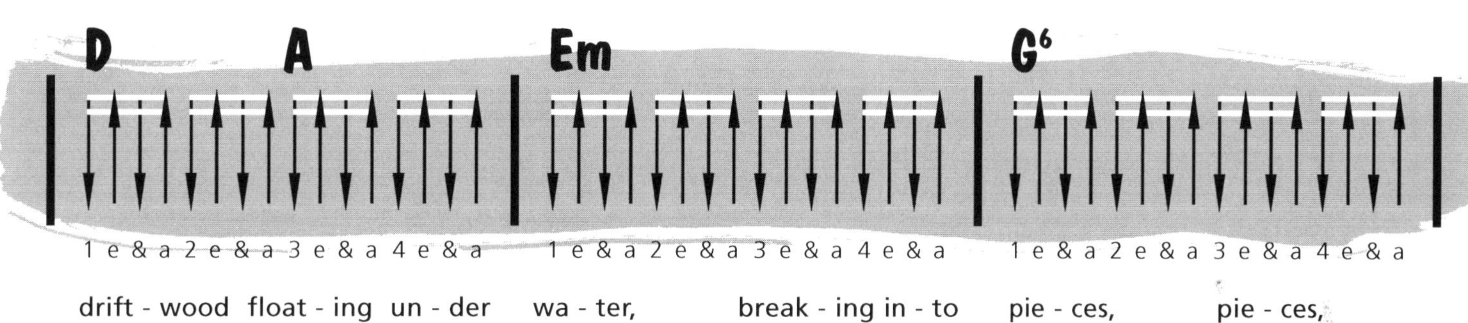

drift - wood float - ing un - der wa - ter, break - ing in - to pie - ces, pie - ces,

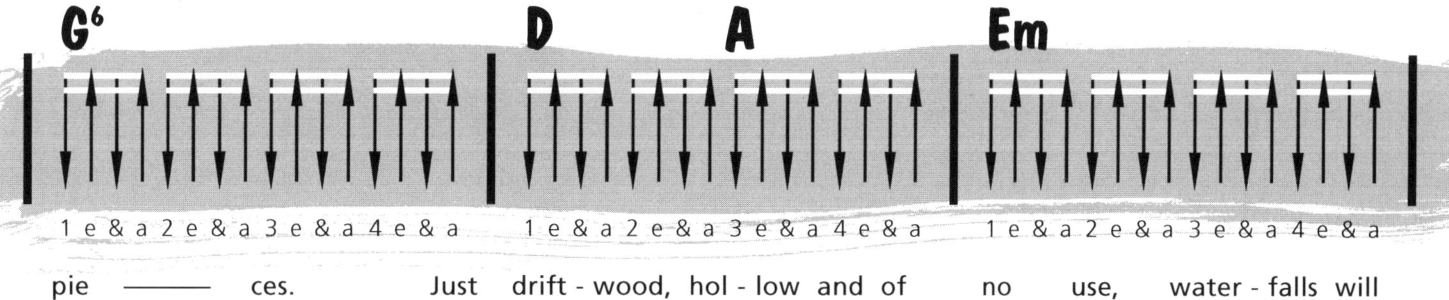

pie ——— ces. Just drift - wood, hol - low and of no use, water - falls will

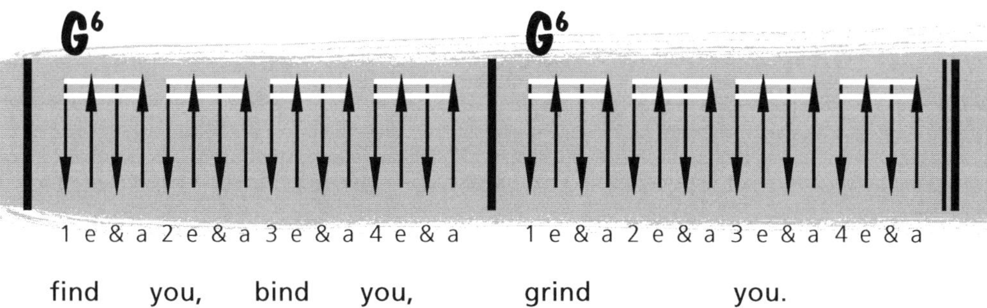

find you, bind you, grind you.

TRACK 6+7

SAIL AWAY

Words & Music by David Gray

Bmadd11 Chord

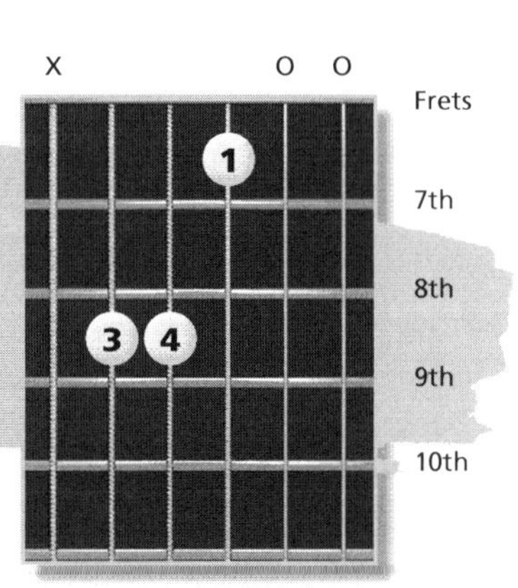

F♯m11 Chord

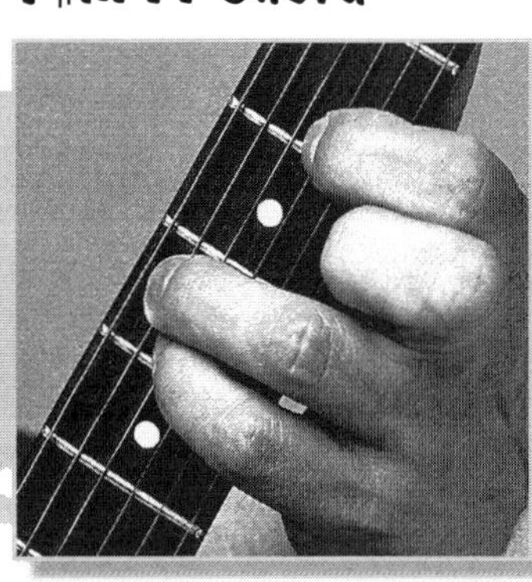

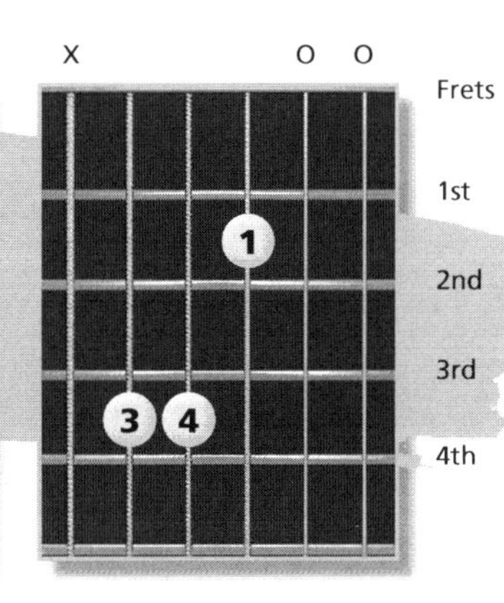

This recent hit for David Gray introduces a new idea you can apply to the chord shapes you have learned.

These two chords are derived from the **F♯m** chord shape you met in Book 1. What has happened is that the barre has been taken off, the first finger has gone to the 3rd string and the 6th string is not played.

This song features a new, complicated off-beat strumming pattern for you to learn. The best way to do this is to listen to the demonstration track and try and 'feel' the rhythm. The other way to learn it is by slowing it right down and counting. Here's how it should go:

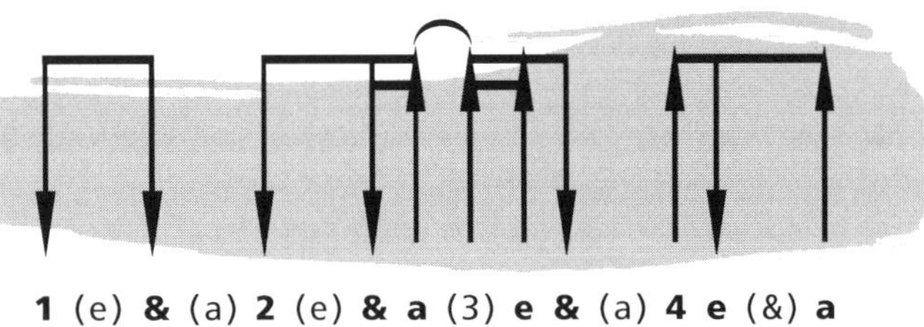

1 (e) **&** (a) **2** (e) **&** **a** (3) **e** **&** (a) **4** **e** (&) **a**

Only count, or play, the bold notes. It looks complicated, but slow it right down and you should get the feel of the rhythm. Then, gradually speed it up.

If you can't manage this you can always play any of the other 4/4 rhythm patterns you've learnt. Just try and pick one that would fit the feel of this song.

CAPO 1ST FRET
1 BAR CLICK + 4 BAR INTRO

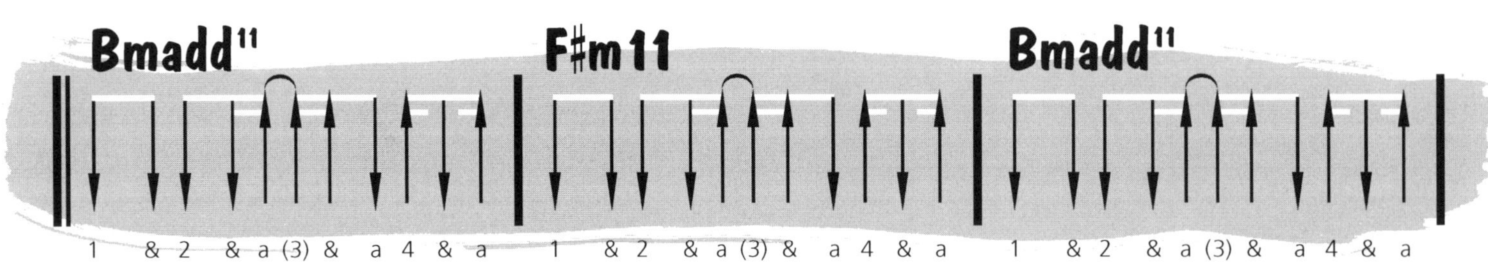

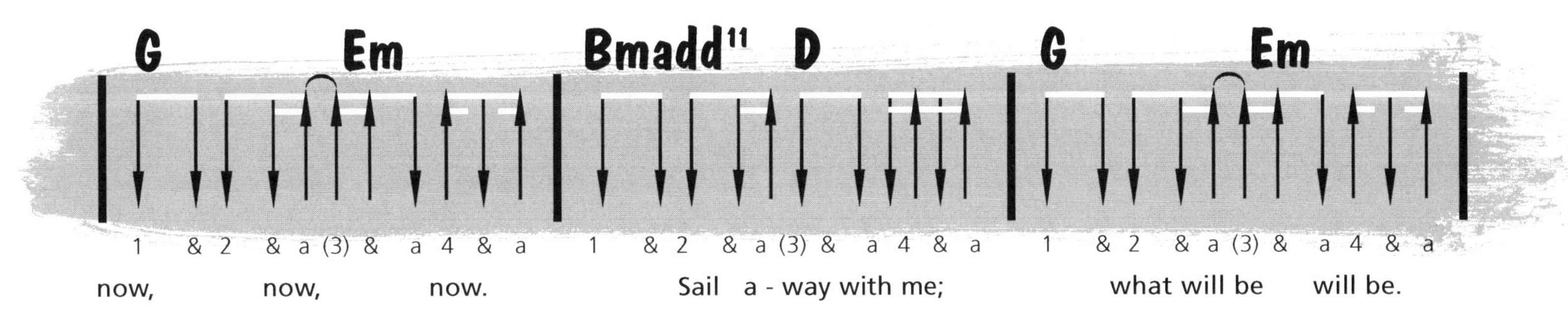
G Em
Bmadd11 D
G Em
1 & 2 & a (3) & a 4 & a
now, now, now.
Sail a - way with me;
what will be will be.

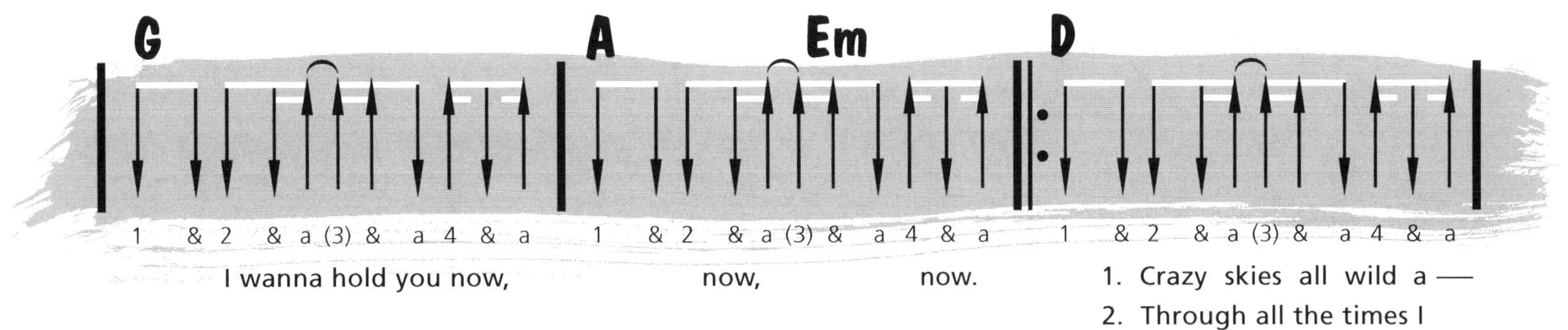
G
A Em
D
1 & 2 & a (3) & a 4 & a
I wanna hold you now,
now, now.
1. Crazy skies all wild a —
2. Through all the times I

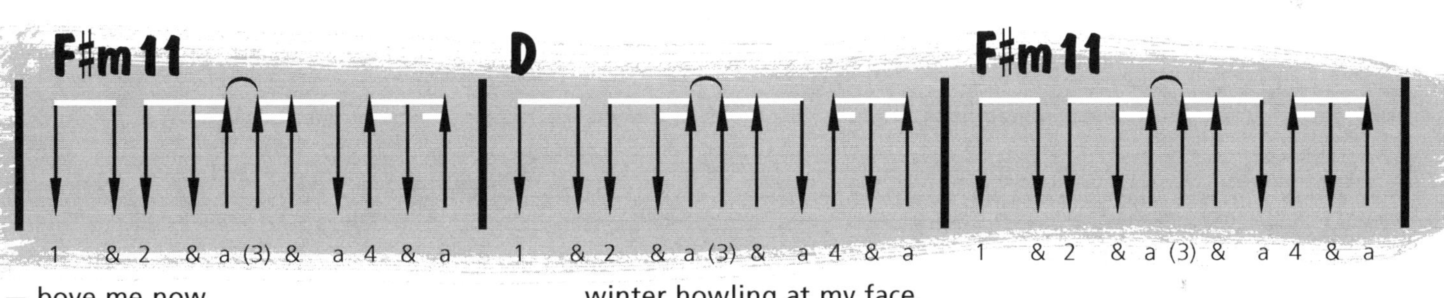
F♯m11
D
F♯m11
1 & 2 & a (3) & a 4 & a
— bove me now,
tast - ed love,
winter howling at my face.
never knew quite what I had.

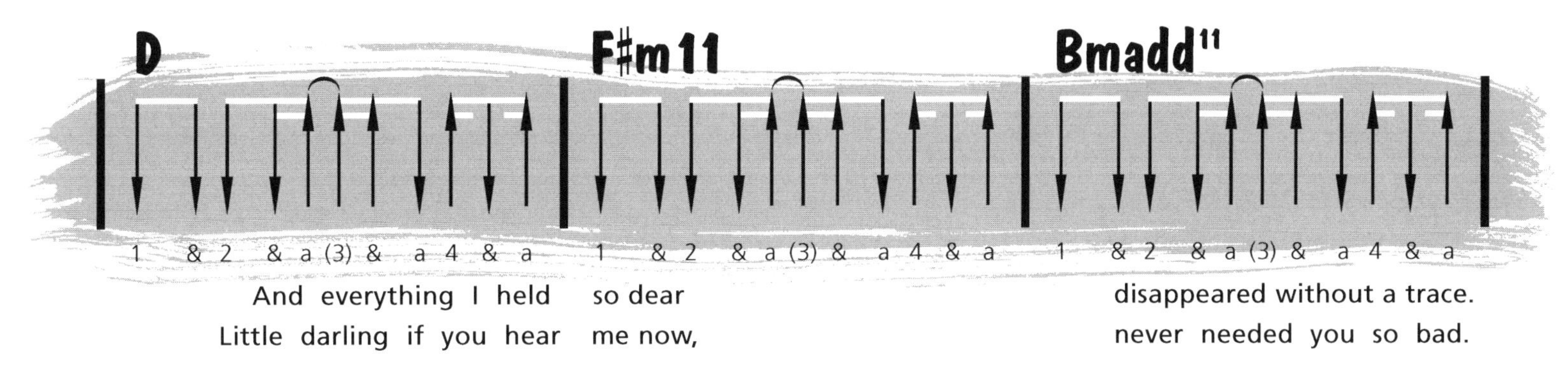
D
F♯m11
Bmadd11
1 & 2 & a (3) & a 4 & a
And everything I held
Little darling if you hear
so dear
me now,
disappeared without a trace.
never needed you so bad.

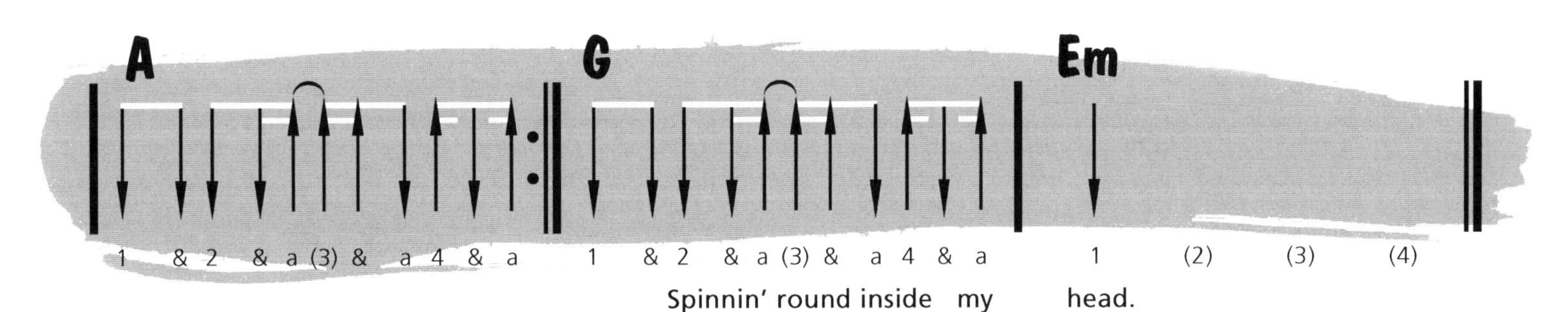
A
G
Em
1 & 2 & a (3) & a 4 & a
1 (2) (3) (4)
Spinnin' round inside my
head.

WILD WOOD

Words & Music by Paul Weller

F♯m/B Chord

Em7 Chord

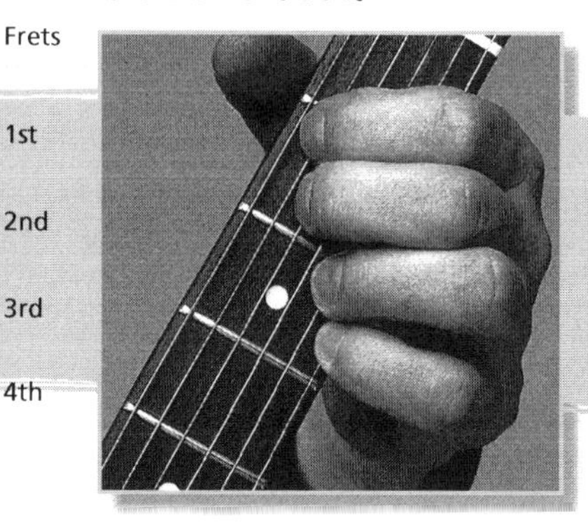

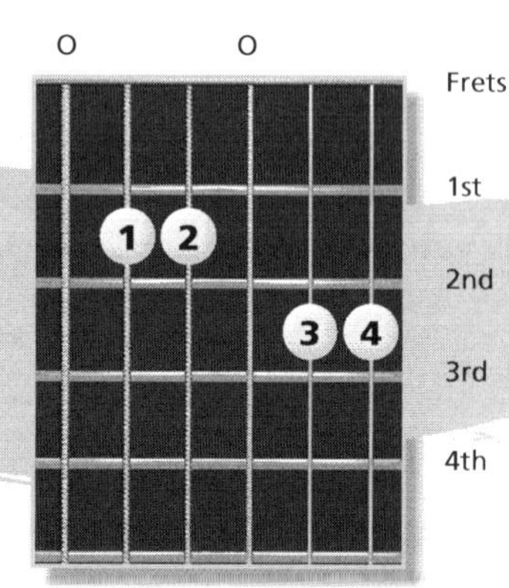

Paul Weller

This 1993 hit by Paul Weller has a relaxed acoustic feel that is quite easy to reproduce. There are three new chord shapes for you.

The **Em7** is a less common shape for this chord than the **Em7** you learned in Book One, but makes more sense harmonically for this song. The **F♯7♯5♭9** is an even rarer chord and helps to give '**Wild Wood**' its slightly jazzy quality.

F♯7♯5♭9 Chord

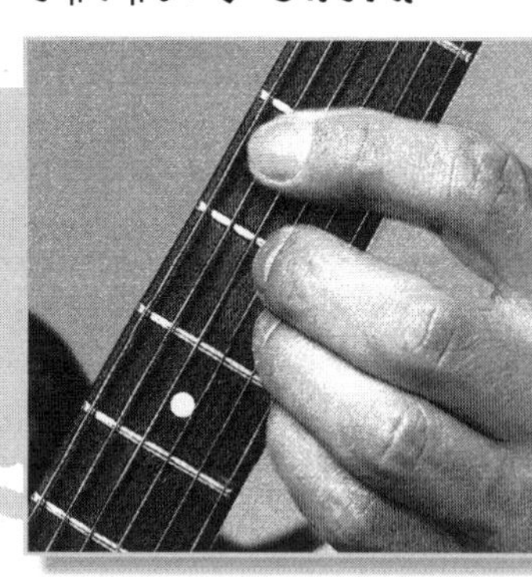

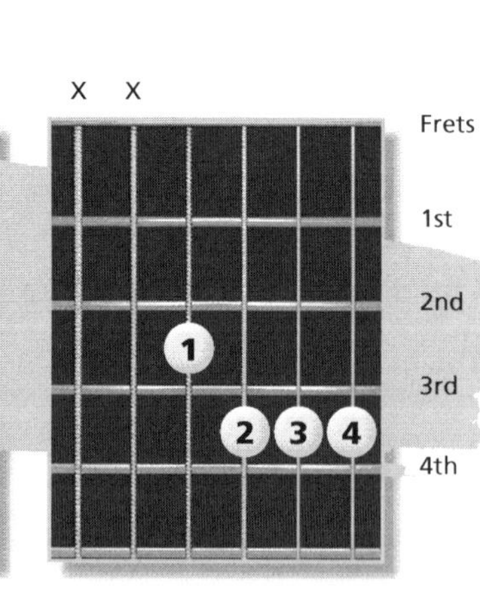

The **Bm** chord is the standard **Bm barre** shape and can be played by using the **C♯m** shape in Book 1 moved down two frets.

With the strumming watch out for the quick up and down that comes on the last beat of the bar.

1 BAR CLICK + 4 BAR INTRO

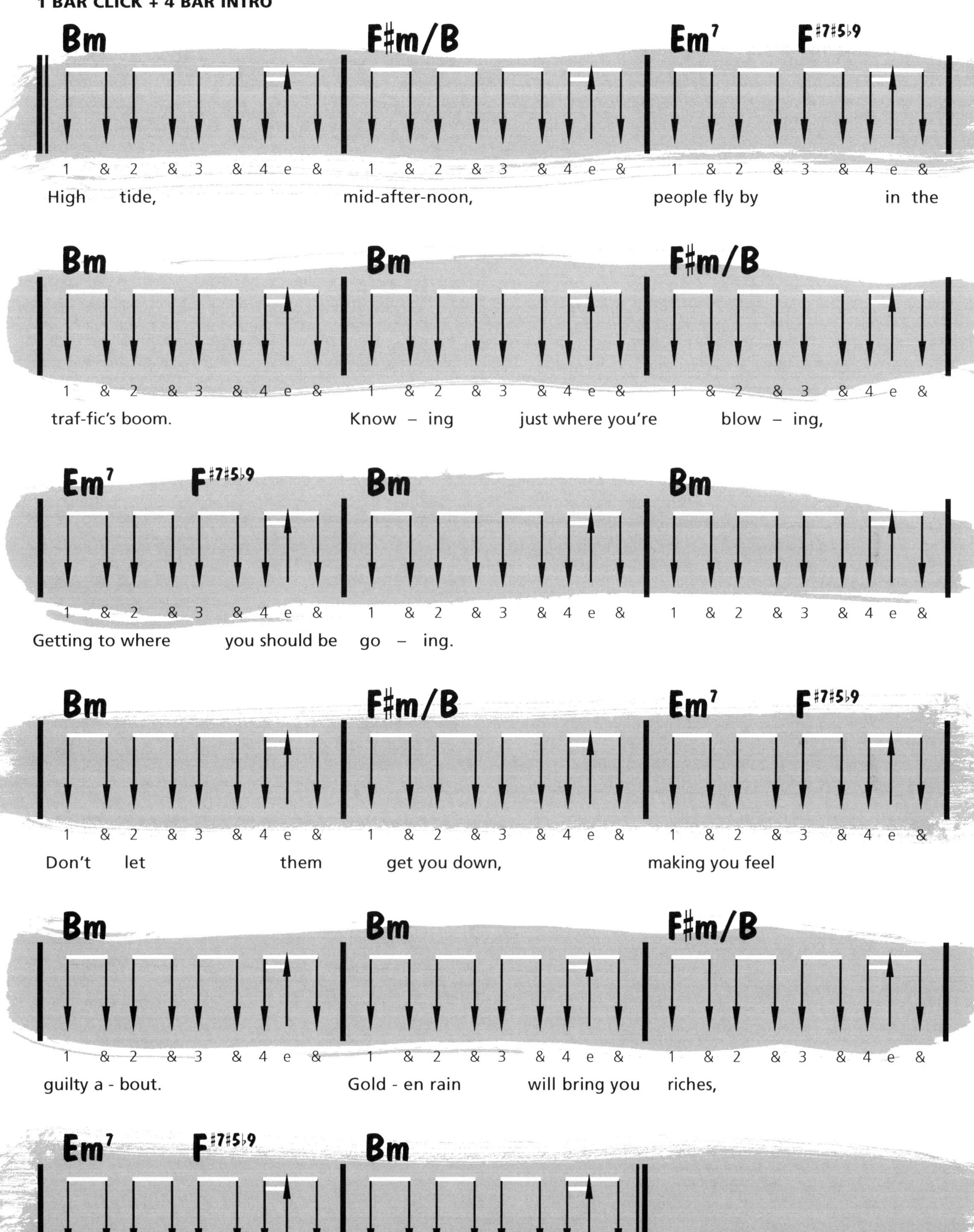

ROLL WITH IT

Words & Music by Noel Gallagher

'Roll With It' was one of several hit singles taken from Oasis' huge album *(What's The Story) Morning Glory?* (1995). It is a good example of how effective chord changes can be made by adapting a few shapes, and how you can adapt shapes so you don't always need to move all your fingers.

For this song we need four new shapes: **A7**, **C7**, **Cadd9** and **G/B**, which are pretty simple, straightforward open chords. The seventh chords give the intro a hard, no-nonsense rock sound.

Cadd9 Chord

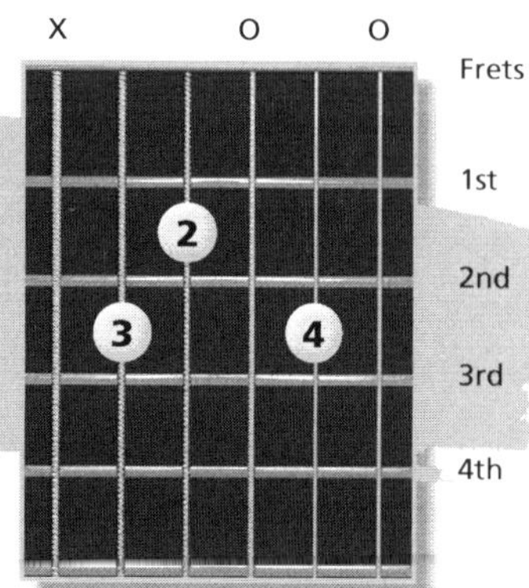

A7 Chord

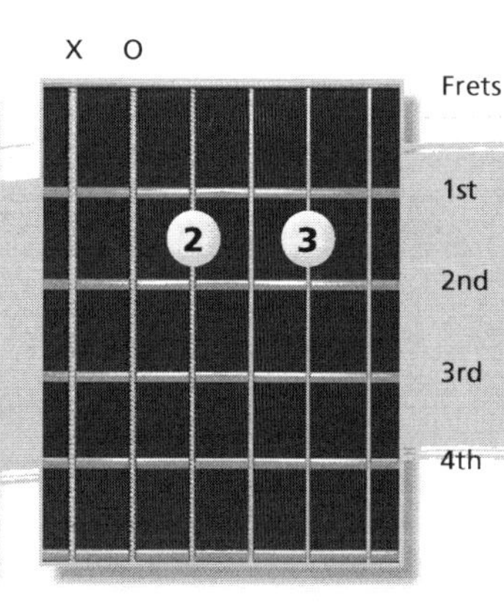

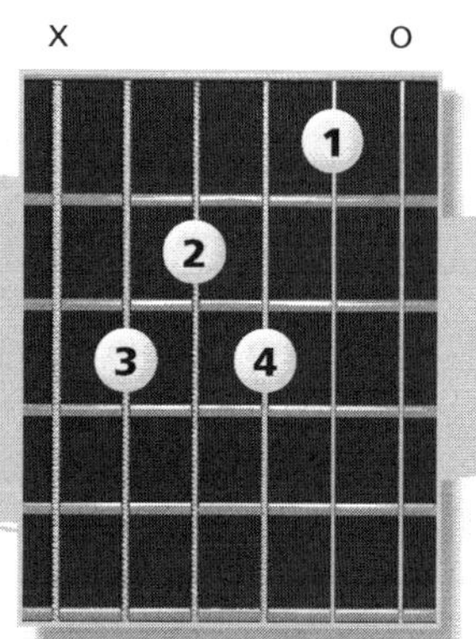

Most of the strumming in 'Roll With It' is straight 8ths, with examples of omitted off-beat strums from time to time.

These little variations help to make your strumming more interesting than if you played 8ths all the time. Letting a chord ring for a beat or two, or coming back in on an offbeat are some of the ways of making rhythms more interesting.

G/B Chord

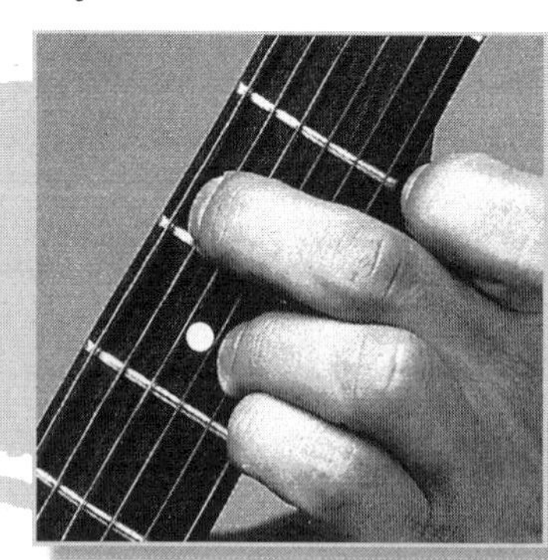

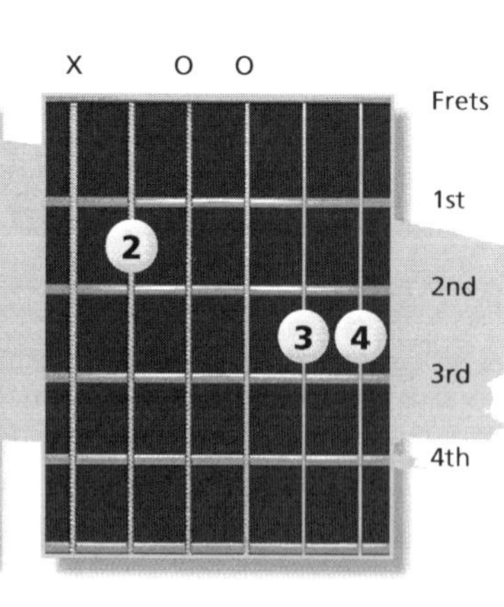

1 BAR CLICK INTRO

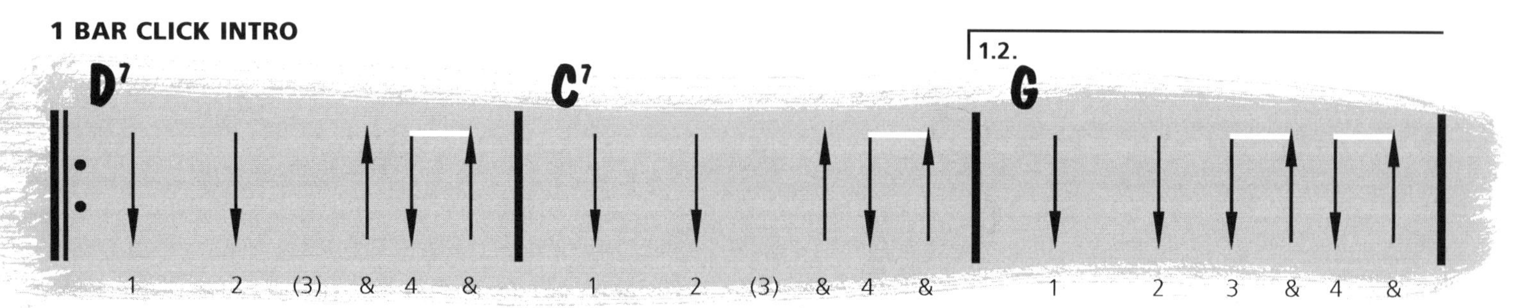

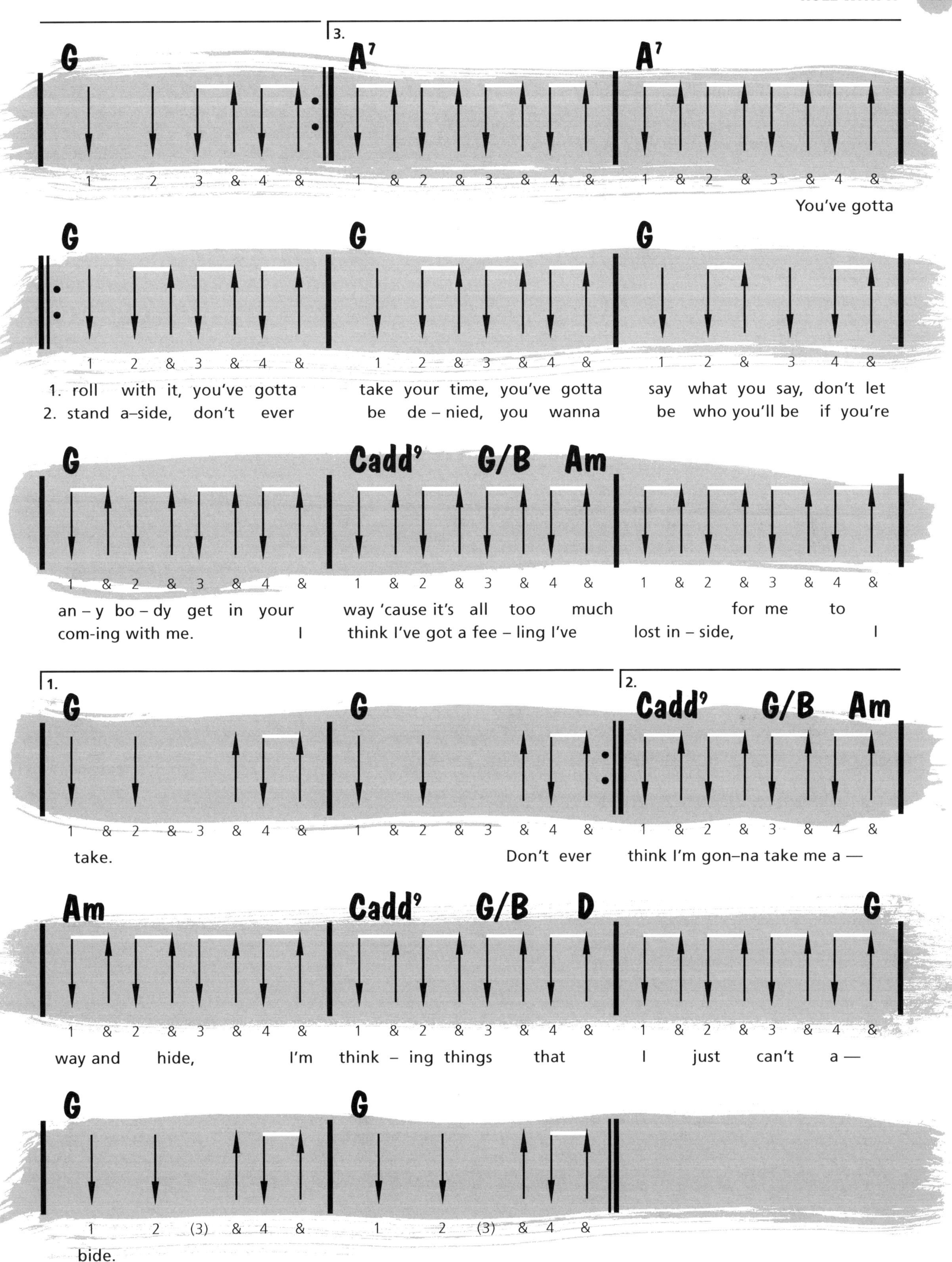
3.
G
A7
A7
1 2 3 & 4 &
1 & 2 & 3 & 4 &
1 & 2 & 3 & 4 &
You've gotta
G
G
G
1 2 & 3 & 4 &
1 2 & 3 & 4 &
1 2 & 3 4 &
1. roll with it, you've gotta
2. stand a–side, don't ever
take your time, you've gotta
be de – nied, you wanna
say what you say, don't let
be who you'll be if you're
G
Cadd9 G/B Am
1 & 2 & 3 & 4 &
1 & 2 & 3 & 4 &
1 & 2 & 3 & 4 &
an – y bo – dy get in your
com-ing with me. I
way 'cause it's all too much
think I've got a fee – ling I've
for me to
lost in – side, I
1.
2.
G
G
Cadd9 G/B Am
1 & 2 & 3 & 4 &
1 & 2 & 3 & 4 &
1 & 2 & 3 & 4 &
take.
Don't ever
think I'm gon–na take me a —
Am
Cadd9 G/B D
G
1 & 2 & 3 & 4 &
1 & 2 & 3 & 4 &
1 & 2 & 3 & 4 &
way and hide, I'm
think – ing things that
I just can't a —
G
G
1 2 (3) & 4 &
1 2 (3) & 4 &
bide.

20TH CENTURY BOY

Words & Music by Marc Bolan

Marc Bolan (T.Rex)

This classic slice of glam rock was a hit for T.Rex first in 1973, then in 1991 after use on a Levi's commercial, and also featured on the soundtrack of the film *Billy Elliot*. '20th Century Boy' uses the chords E, A and B - all of which you have played before.

The strum for '**20th Century Boy**' is mostly 8ths. Watch out for the 8th/16th/16th figure on the last beat of bar 2, which can also be found elsewhere in the song. You can also try learning the song's famous riff (see tab below).

The arrow indicates that the 2nd fret (**F♯**) on the bottom **E** string is bent a semitone, and is called a semitone, or half-tone bend. To play this, bend push the string upwards quickly after striking the note.

Here is the song's opening guitar riff:

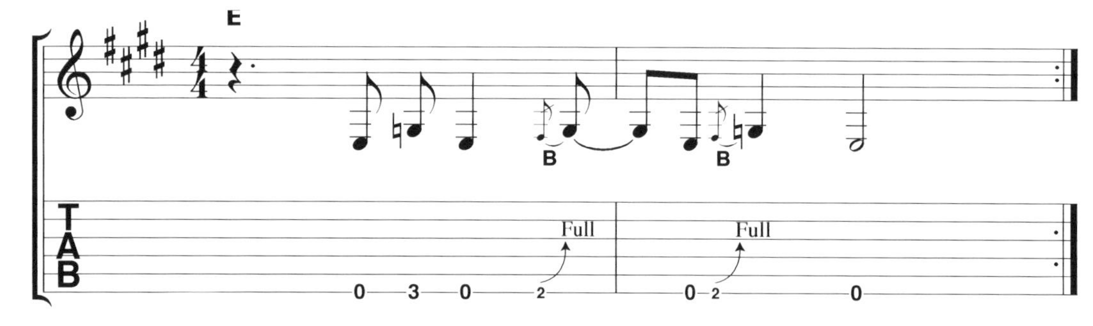

2 BAR CLICK + 2 BAR INTRO

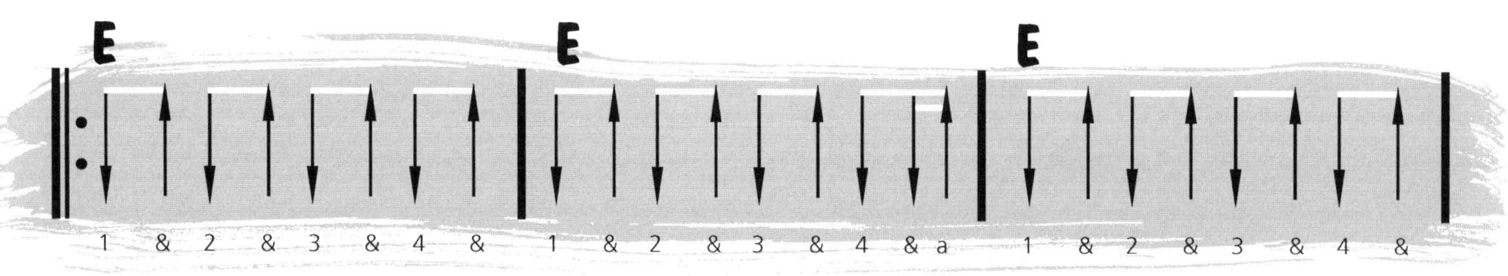

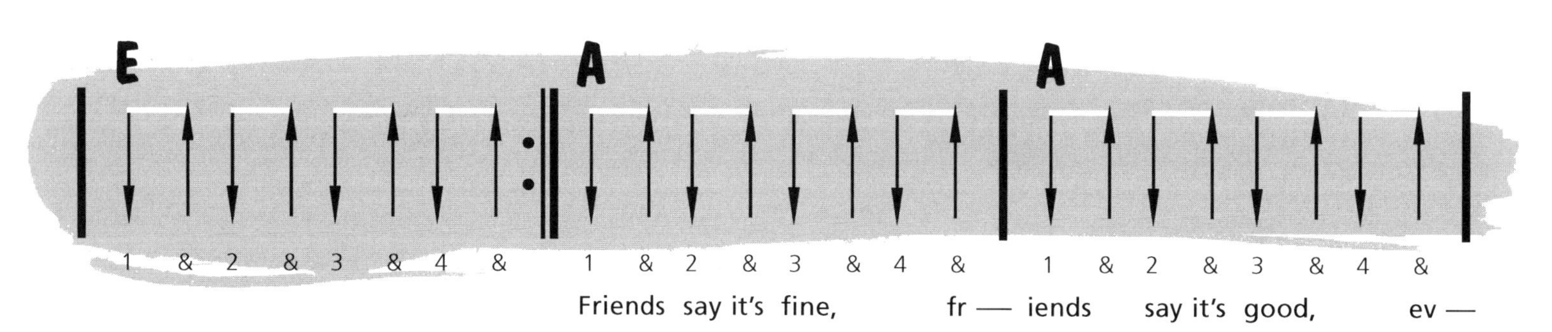

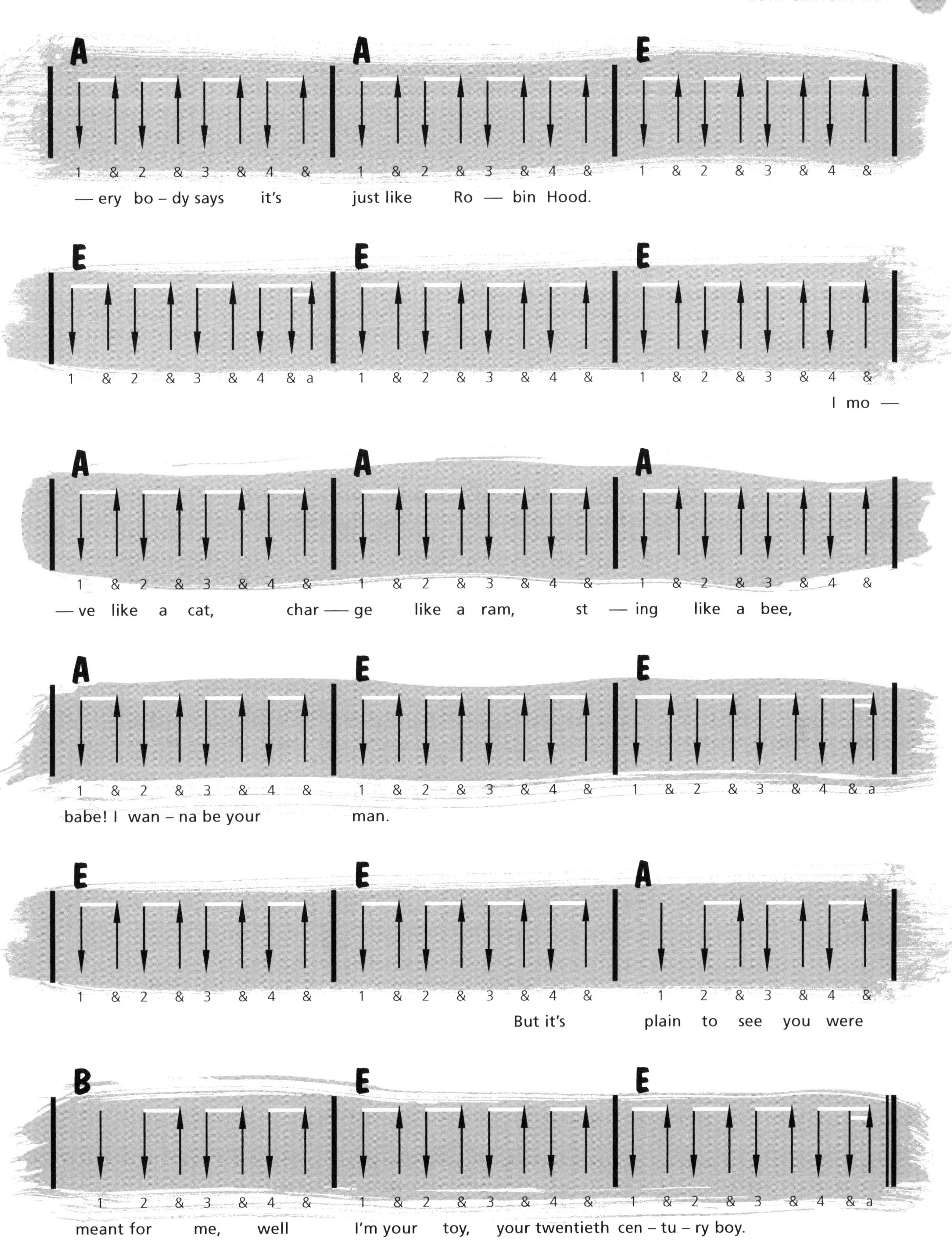
A A E
1 & 2 & 3 & 4 & 1 & 2 & 3 & 4 & 1 & 2 & 3 & 4 &
— ery bo – dy says it's just like Ro — bin Hood.
E E E
1 & 2 & 3 & 4 & a 1 & 2 & 3 & 4 & 1 & 2 & 3 & 4 &
I mo —
A A A
1 & 2 & 3 & 4 & 1 & 2 & 3 & 4 & 1 & 2 & 3 & 4 &
— ve like a cat, char — ge like a ram, st — ing like a bee,
A E E
1 & 2 & 3 & 4 & 1 & 2 & 3 & 4 & 1 & 2 & 3 & 4 & a
babe! I wan – na be your man.
E E A
1 & 2 & 3 & 4 & 1 & 2 & 3 & 4 & 1 2 & 3 & 4 &
But it's plain to see you were
B E E
1 2 & 3 & 4 & 1 & 2 & 3 & 4 & 1 & 2 & 3 & 4 & a
meant for me, well I'm your toy, your twentieth cen – tu – ry boy.

SHE LOVES YOU

Words & Music by John Lennon & Paul McCartney

This great example of the early 'Fab Four' features the chords G, Em, Bm, D, D7 and A, all of which you know. The Cm can be played by taking the Bm from 'Wild Wood' and moving it up one fret.

'She Loves You' has two famous guitar fills. Here they are:

GUITAR FILL 1

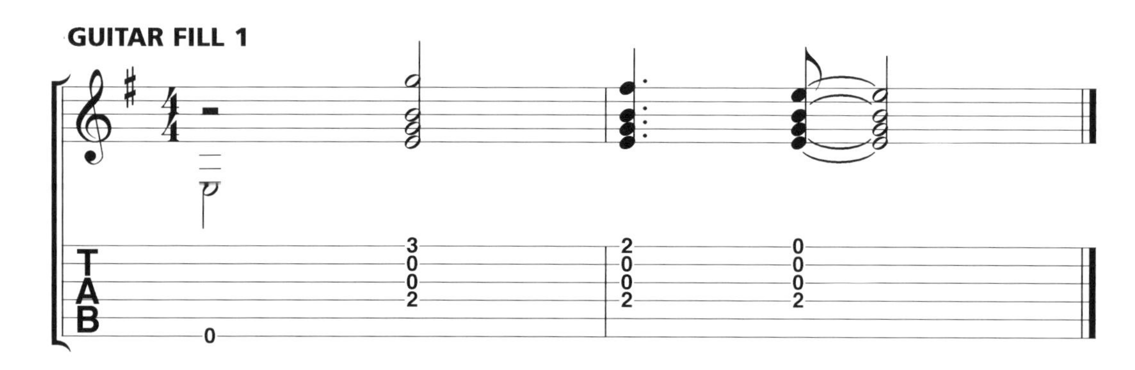

GUITAR FILL 2

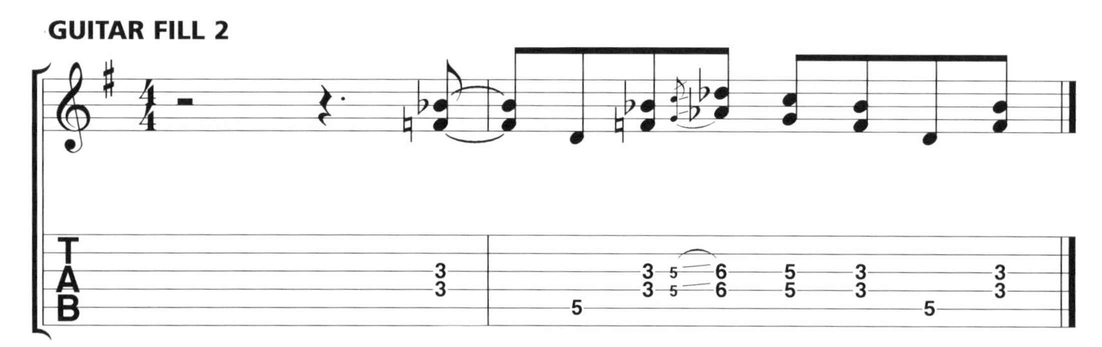

CAPO 1ST FRET
2 BAR CLICK + 8 BAR INTRO

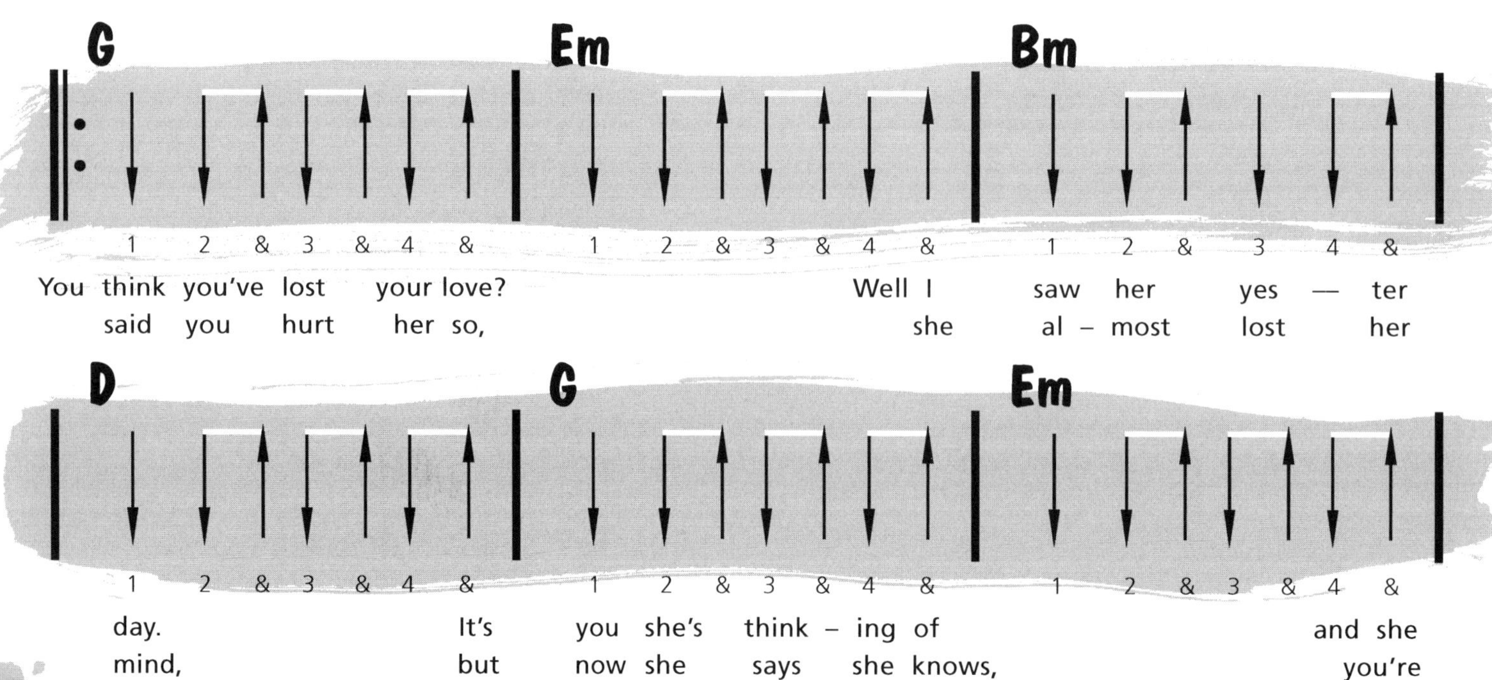

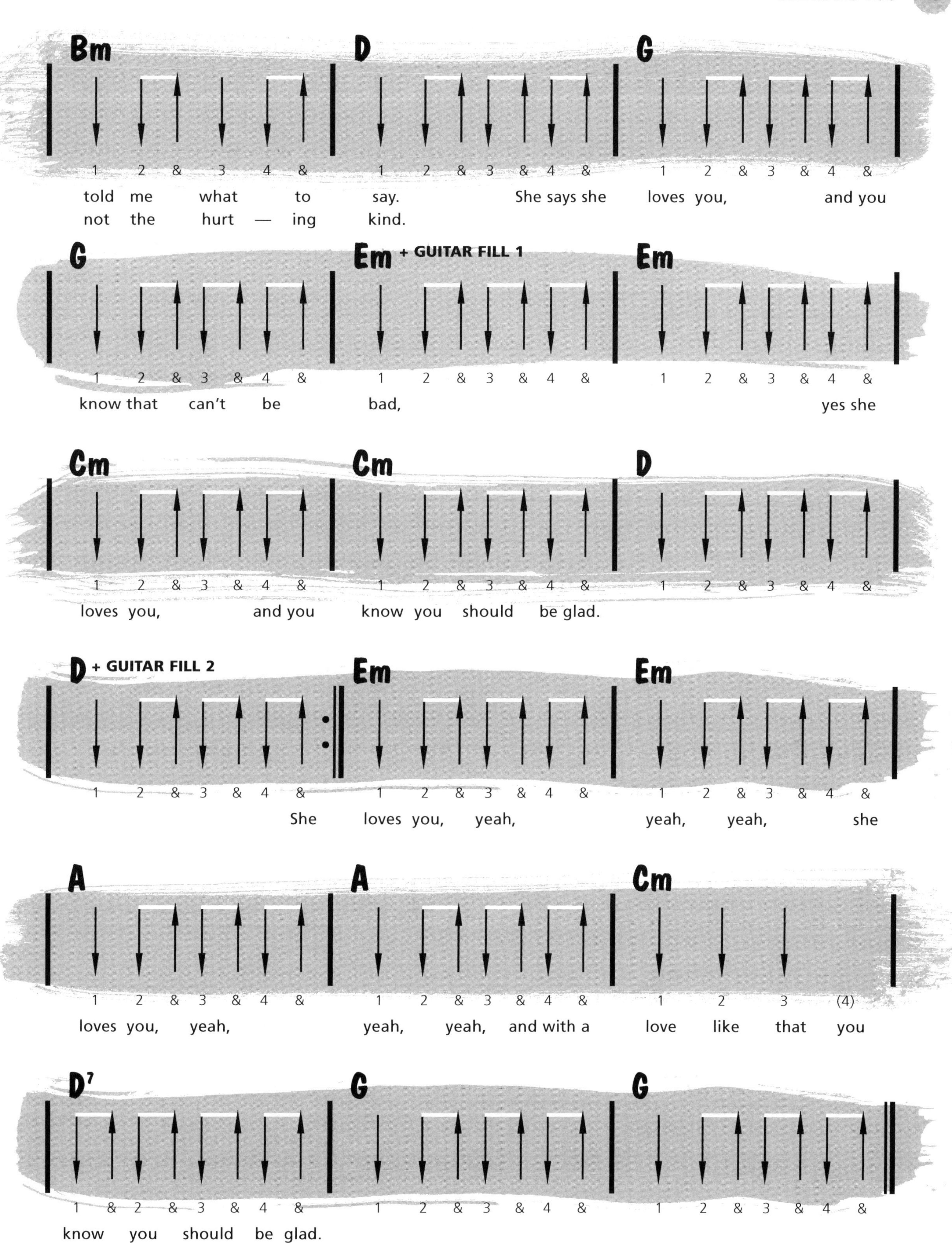
Bm
D
G
1 2 & 3 4 &
1 2 & 3 & 4 &
1 2 & 3 & 4 &
told me what to say. She says she loves you, and you
not the hurt — ing kind.
G
Em + GUITAR FILL 1
Em
1 2 & 3 & 4 &
1 2 & 3 & 4 &
1 2 & 3 & 4 &
know that can't be bad, yes she
Cm
Cm
D
1 2 & 3 & 4 &
1 2 & 3 & 4 &
1 2 & 3 & 4 &
loves you, and you know you should be glad.
D + GUITAR FILL 2
Em
Em
1 2 & 3 & 4 &
1 2 & 3 & 4 &
1 2 & 3 & 4 &
She loves you, yeah, yeah, yeah, she
A
A
Cm
1 2 & 3 & 4 &
1 2 & 3 & 4 &
1 2 3 (4)
loves you, yeah, yeah, yeah, and with a love like that you
D7
G
G
1 & 2 & 3 & 4 &
1 2 & 3 & 4 &
1 2 & 3 & 4 &
know you should be glad.

I SHOT THE SHERIFF

Words & Music by Bob Marley

Bm7 Chord

Cmaj7 Chord

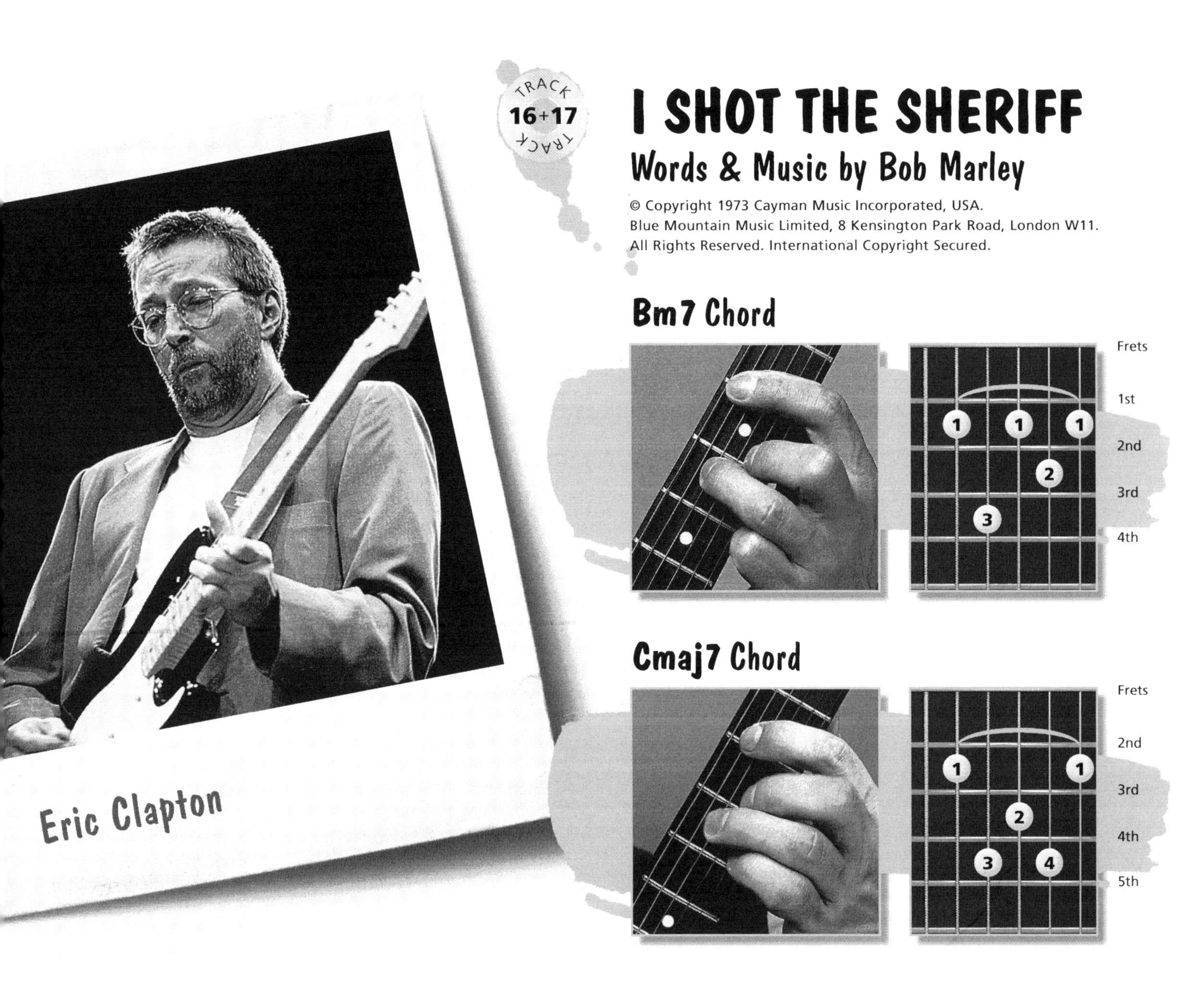

Eric Clapton had a smash hit with this Bob Marley song in 1974.

This song has a reggae feel due to the fact that you strum on the 'off-beats' of the bar – the 2nd and 4th. Watch out for the rhythm change from the chorus to the verse.

There are two new chords, **Bm7** and **Cmaj7** (see above).

Cmaj7 can also be played by holding down a **C** chord and lifting your 1st finger off the 2nd string. However this barre version sounds better here and makes the change to **Bm7** easier (both barred and the third finger is a guide finger).

To play along with the CD simply put a capo on at the third fret. This will put you in the right key as the original without changing any of the riff fingering or the chord shapes.

CAPO 3RD FRET
1 BAR CLICK INTRO

CHORUS

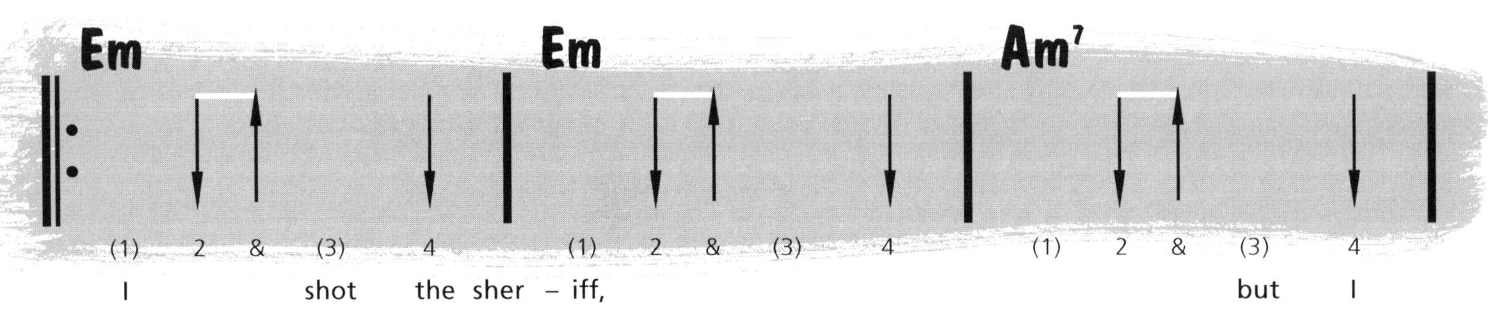

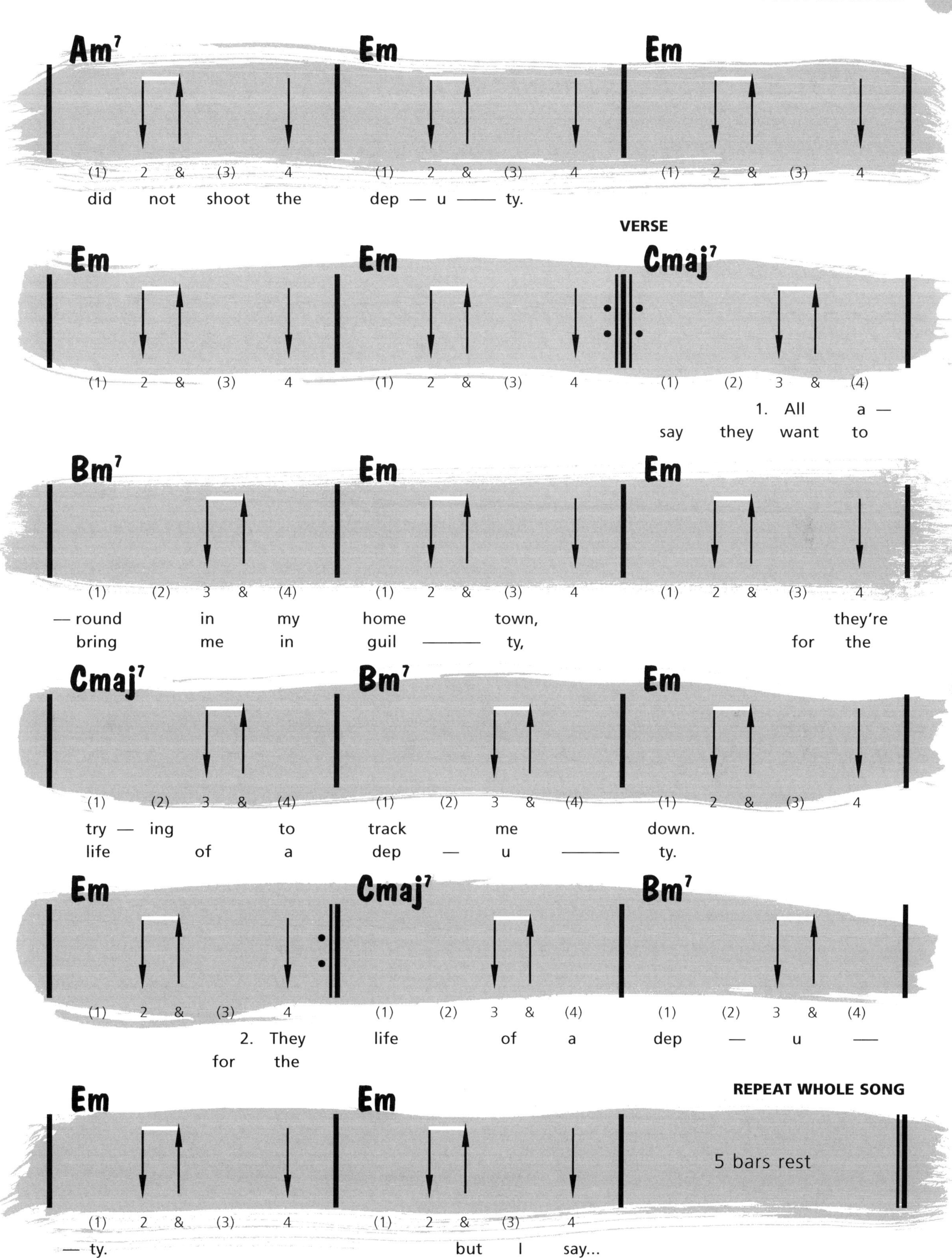
Am7
Em
Em
(1) 2 & (3) 4
(1) 2 & (3) 4
(1) 2 & (3) 4
did not shoot the dep — u —— ty.
VERSE
Em
Em
Cmaj7
(1) 2 & (3) 4
(1) 2 & (3) 4
(1) (2) 3 & (4)
1. All a —
say they want to
Bm7
Em
Em
(1) (2) 3 & (4)
(1) 2 & (3) 4
(1) 2 & (3) 4
— round in my home town, they're
bring me in guil ——— ty, for the
Cmaj7
Bm7
Em
(1) (2) 3 & (4)
(1) (2) 3 & (4)
(1) 2 & (3) 4
try — ing to track me down.
life of a dep — u ——— ty.
Em
Cmaj7
Bm7
(1) 2 & (3) 4
(1) (2) 3 & (4)
(1) (2) 3 & (4)
2. They life of a dep — u —
for the
Em
Em
REPEAT WHOLE SONG
5 bars rest
(1) 2 & (3) 4
(1) 2 & (3) 4
— ty. but I say...

18+19 TRACK

SUNNY AFTERNOON

Words & Music by Ray Davies

To play The Kinks' No.1 from the summer of 1966 you will need one new chord, D minor:

Along with **Am** and **Em**, **Dm** is the most popular of the open string minor shapes. It isn't as full-sounding as the other two because the root note is only as low as the open fourth string and only four strings are played.

'**Sunny Afternoon**' gets some of its jaunty feel from the fact that the rhythm is lightly swung. As with '**Rock Around The Clock**' this means that the pairs of 8ths are not even in length. Each beat feels as though it is dividing into three. So tap the beat, count 1,2,3, and make your down strum last for 1,2, and your up strum falls on the '3'.

Dm Chord

When you are working out how to do a chord change always look to see if there is a guide finger. This is a finger that either moves up or down the same string or doesn't move at all. So if you change from **C** to **F (full barre)** there is no need for the 3rd finger to move. If you change from **A** to **Dm** there is no need for the 2nd finger to move. If you notice these sorts of fingerings you will find chord changing quicker.

Here is the DESCENDING BASS FIGURE that starts the song:

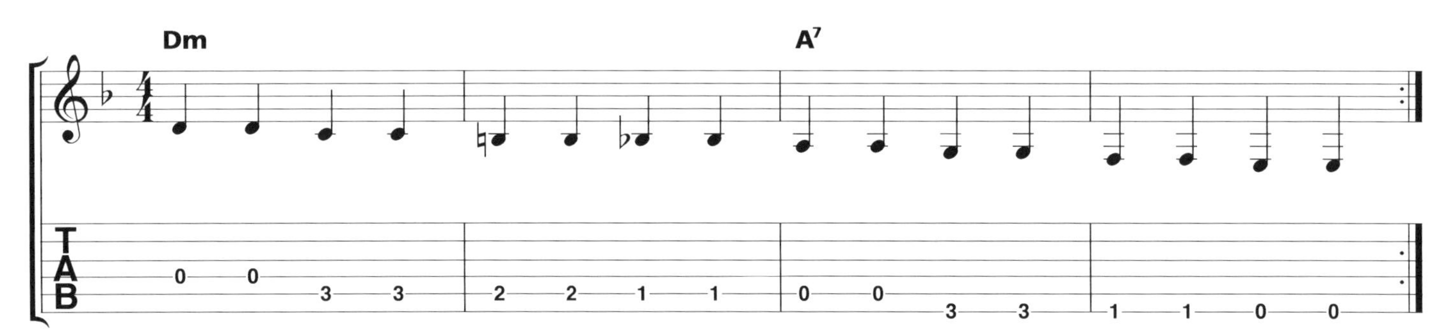

2 BAR CLICK + 8 BAR INTRO

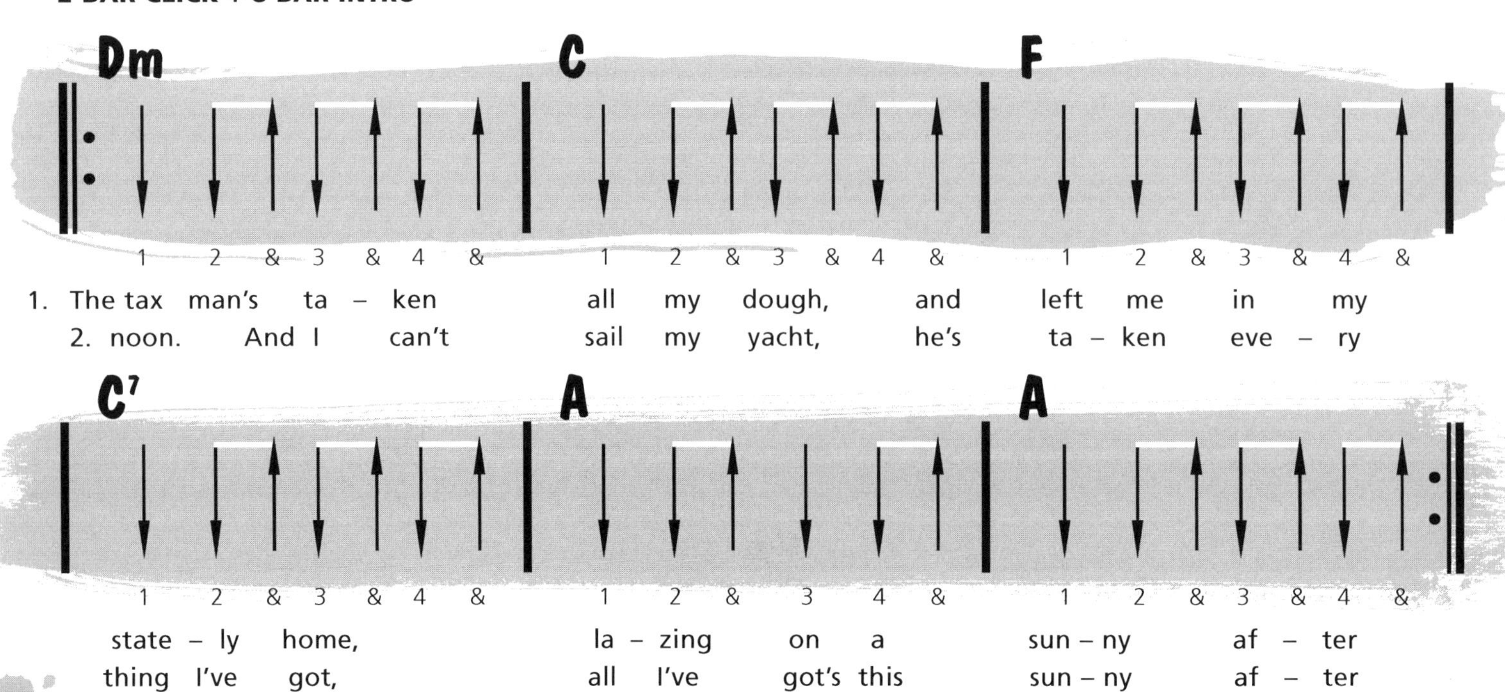

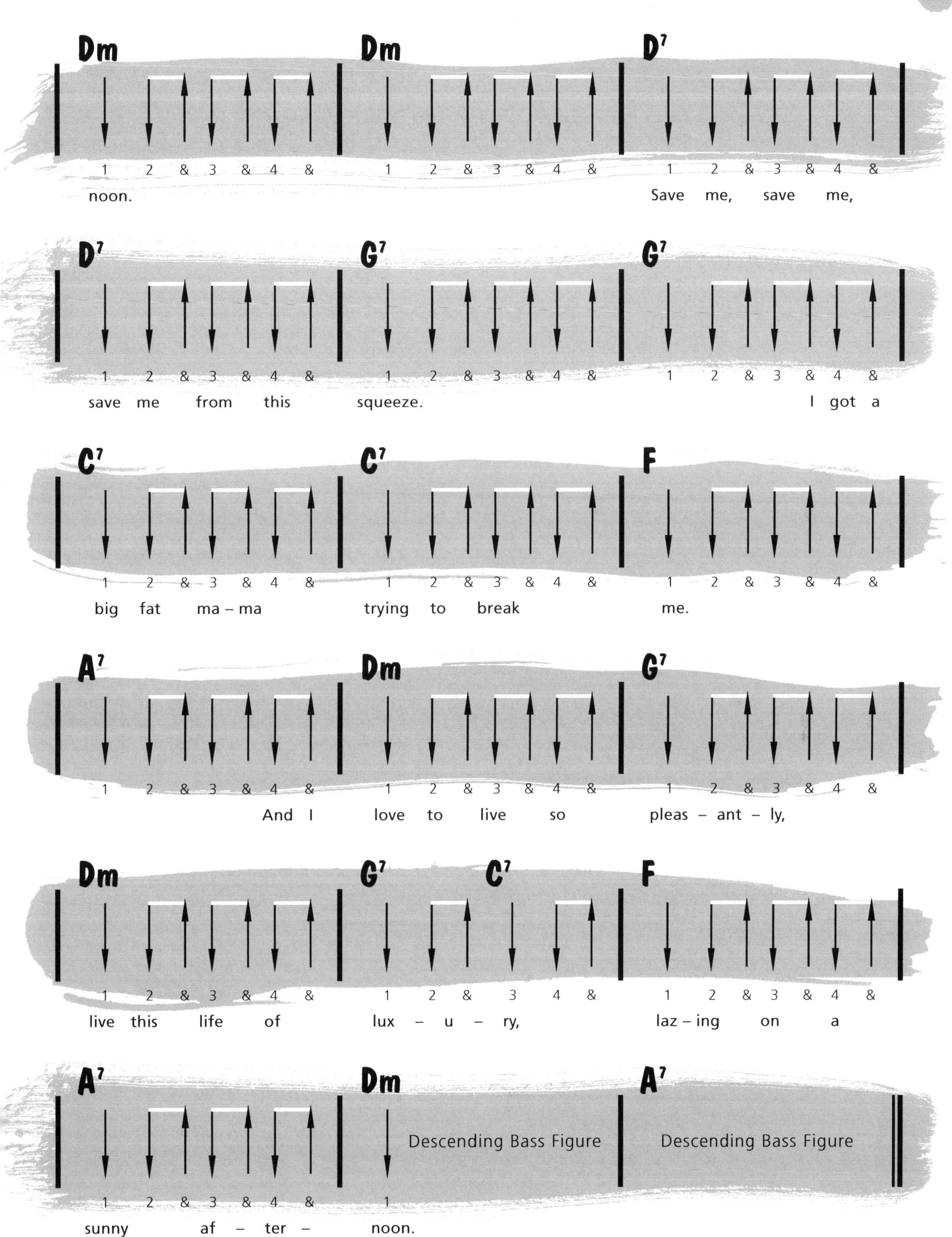
Dm Dm D7
1 2 & 3 & 4 &
noon. Save me, save me,
D7 G7 G7
save me from this squeeze. I got a
C7 C7 F
big fat ma – ma trying to break me.
A7 Dm G7
And I love to live so pleas – ant – ly,
Dm G7 C7 F
live this life of lux – u – ry, laz – ing on a
A7 Dm A7
Descending Bass Figure
Descending Bass Figure
sunny af – ter – noon.

THERE SHE GOES

Words & Music by Lee Mavers

The La's

First recorded by Liverpool group The La's and subsequently covered by U.S. outfit Sixpence None The Richer, this 90s classic is well-suited to the guitar.

The famous chiming guitar figure on the intro is easy to play once you get the hang of the rhythm. When picking the top two strings use alternating down and up strokes with the pick. Unlike strumming, picking single notes requires only a small movement; your arm and even much of your hand will be still.

You can play it throughout the song, or just play the rhythm part on the opposite page. This can be played with a straight-eighth strumming pattern.

GUITAR INTRO

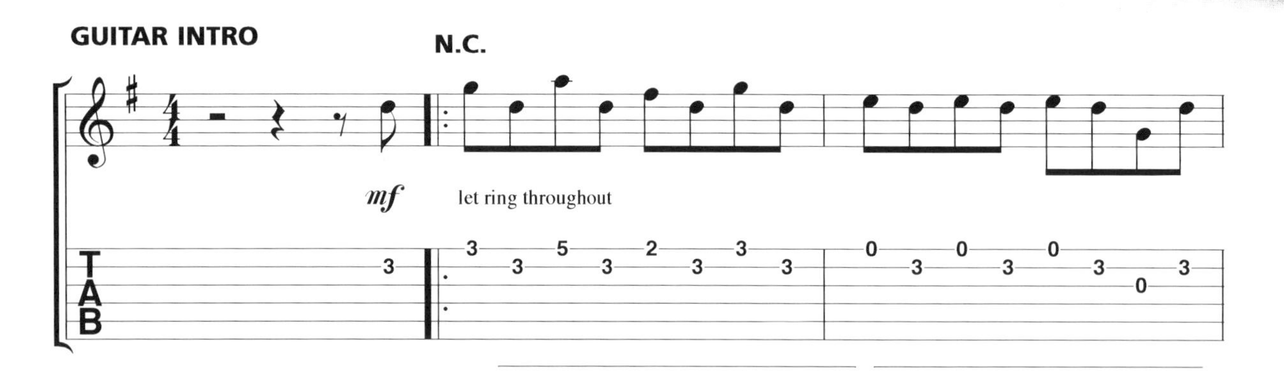

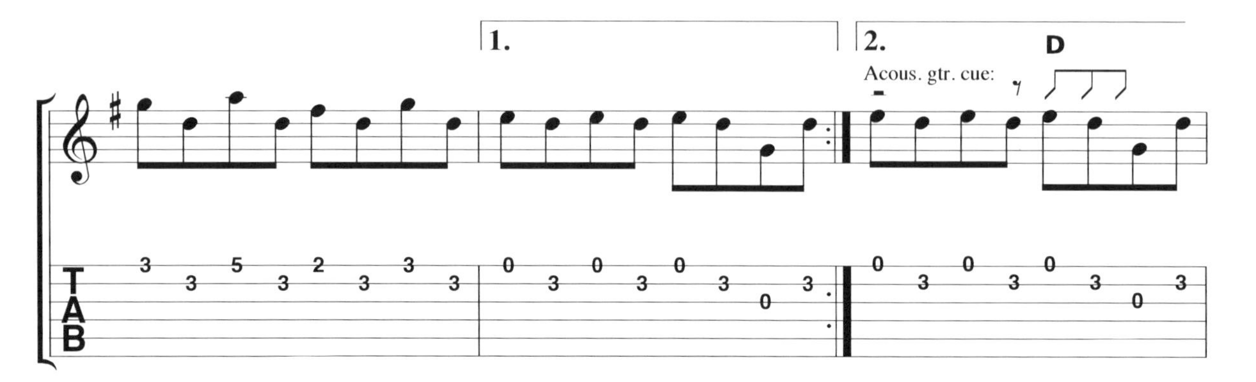

4 BAR INTRO

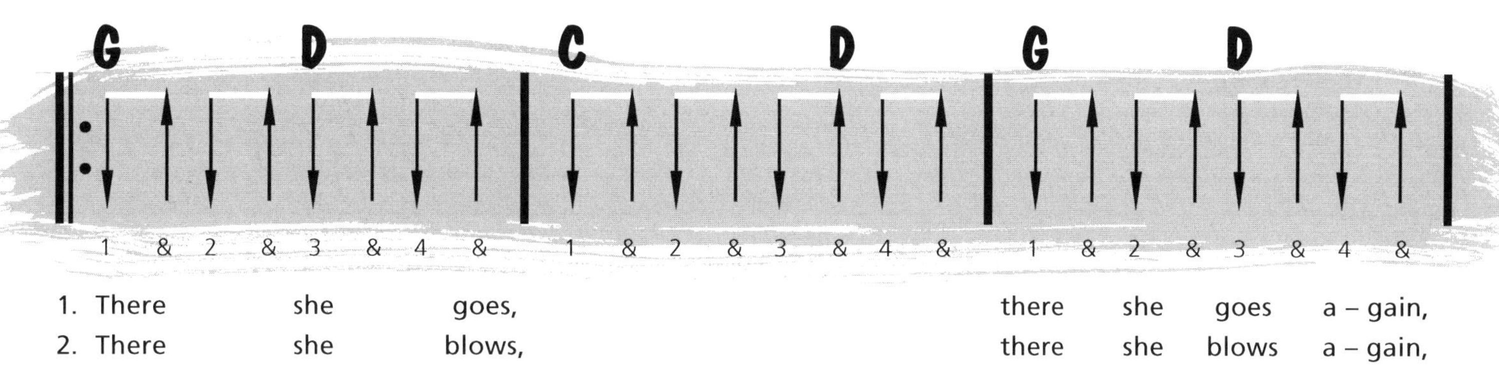
G D C D G D
1 & 2 & 3 & 4 & 1 & 2 & 3 & 4 & 1 & 2 & 3 & 4 &
1. There she goes, there she goes a – gain,
2. There she blows, there she blows a – gain,

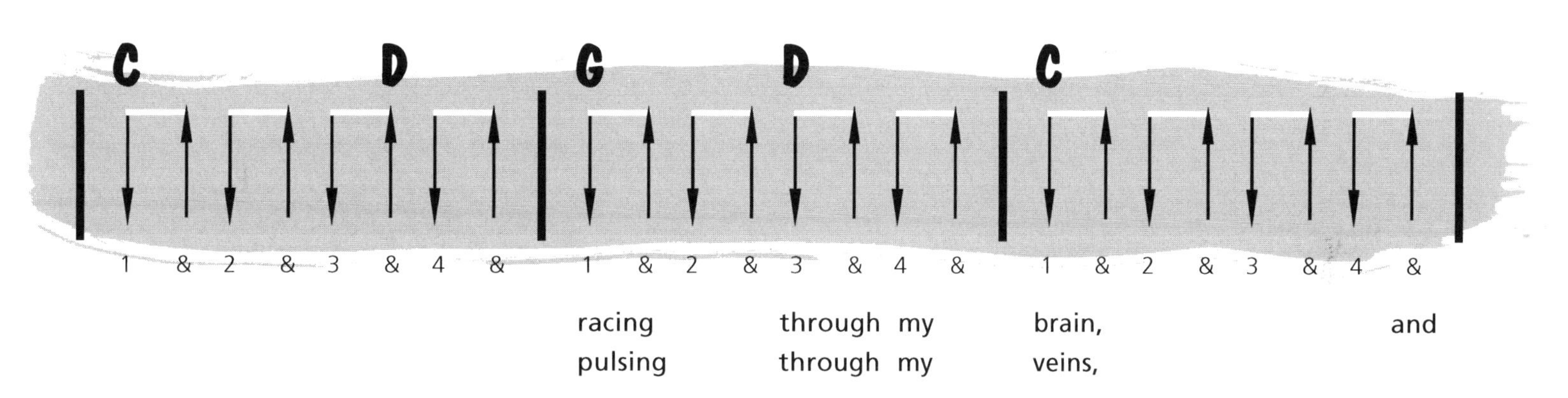
C D G D C
1 & 2 & 3 & 4 & 1 & 2 & 3 & 4 & 1 & 2 & 3 & 4 &
racing through my brain, and
pulsing through my veins,

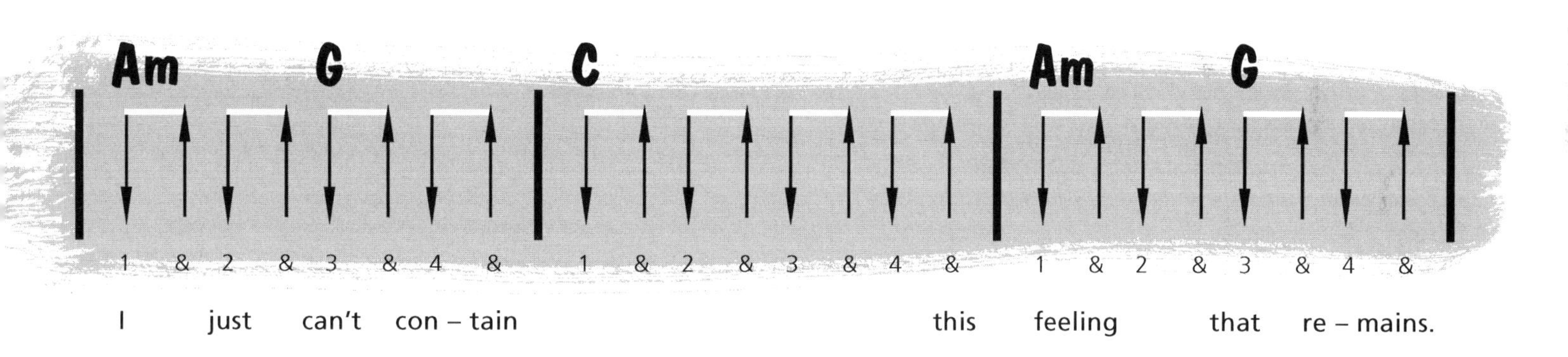
Am G C Am G
1 & 2 & 3 & 4 & 1 & 2 & 3 & 4 & 1 & 2 & 3 & 4 &
I just can't con – tain this feeling that re – mains.

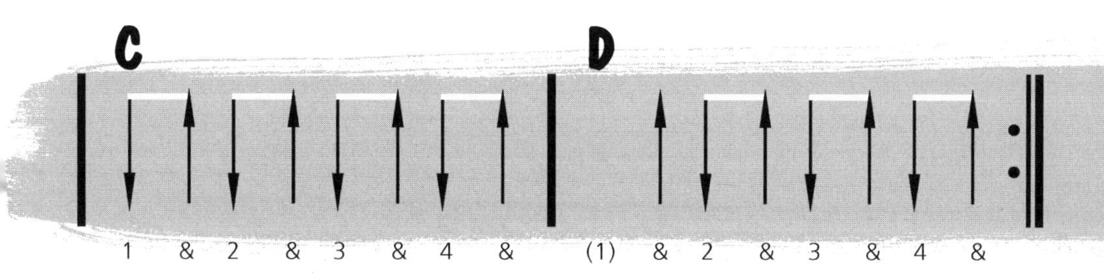
C D
1 & 2 & 3 & 4 & (1) & 2 & 3 & 4 &

HEY JOE

Words & Music by William M. Roberts

Jimi Hendrix

The entire song here is based on a single four-bar chord progression using C, G, D, A, E and E7. Notice the first is the tie sign (⌒) used to tie two notes of the same pitch together so that only the first of the tied notes is played. You can see this in bar 3 of 'Hey Joe'.

To play this bar strum all the marks as shown but leave out the one that falls directly over the 4, letting the previous strum (a chord change to E7) ring instead.

You can also try your hand at this catchy chromatic riff which fits perfectly under the chords and is instantly recognisable as the famous bass riff from the Jimi Hendrix smash hit recording of this song.

A chromatic phrase is one which uses notes that are not properly in key. Chromatic phrases usually feature lots of semitone movement in either direction. The timing is easy because the riff is a straight eight pattern. Practise it very slowly and evenly before attempting to play it at the correct tempo.

Here is the main guitar riff:

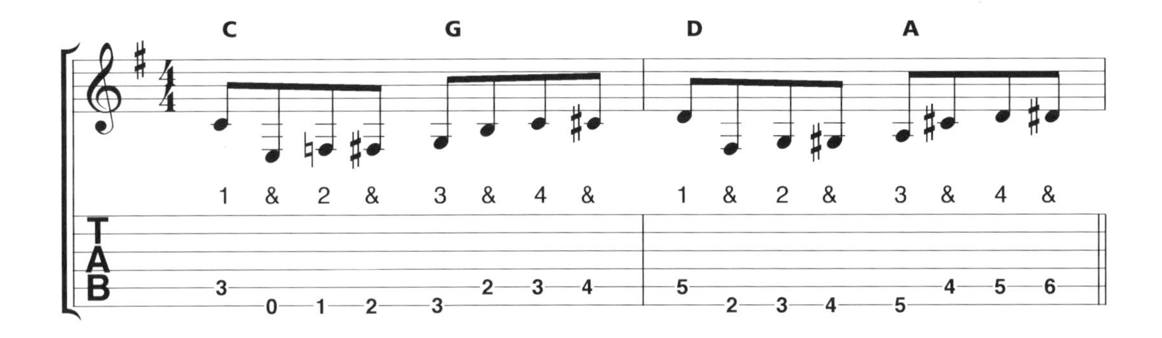

1 BAR CLICK + 3 BAR INTRO

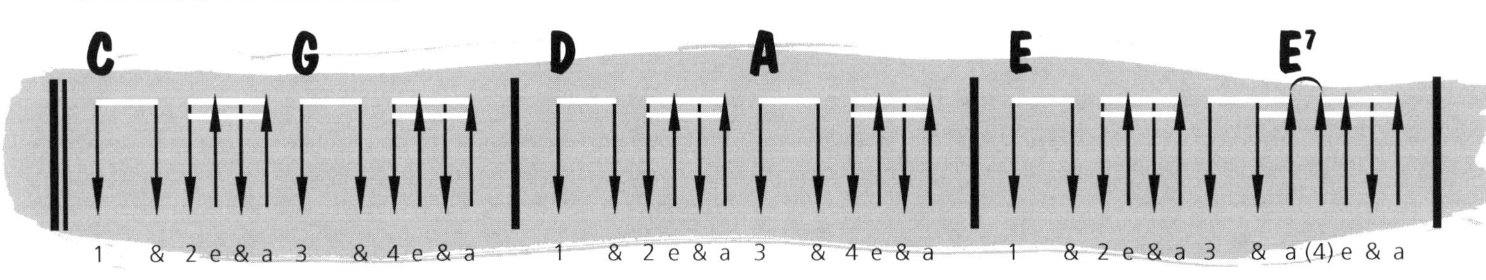

Hey Joe, where you goin' with that gun in your hand?

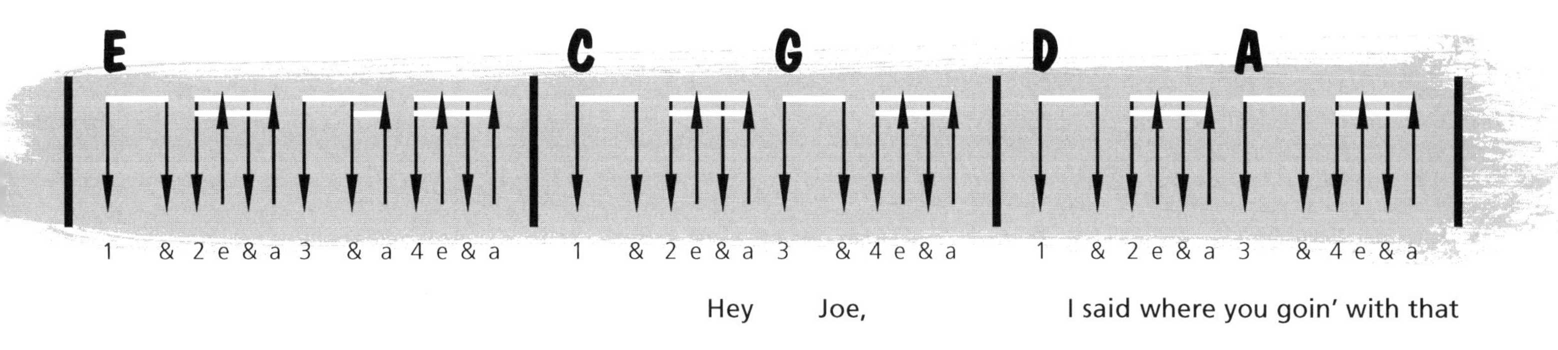
E
C G
D A
1 & 2 e & a 3 & a 4 e & a
1 & 2 e & a 3 & 4 e & a
1 & 2 e & a 3 & 4 e & a
Hey Joe,
I said where you goin' with that

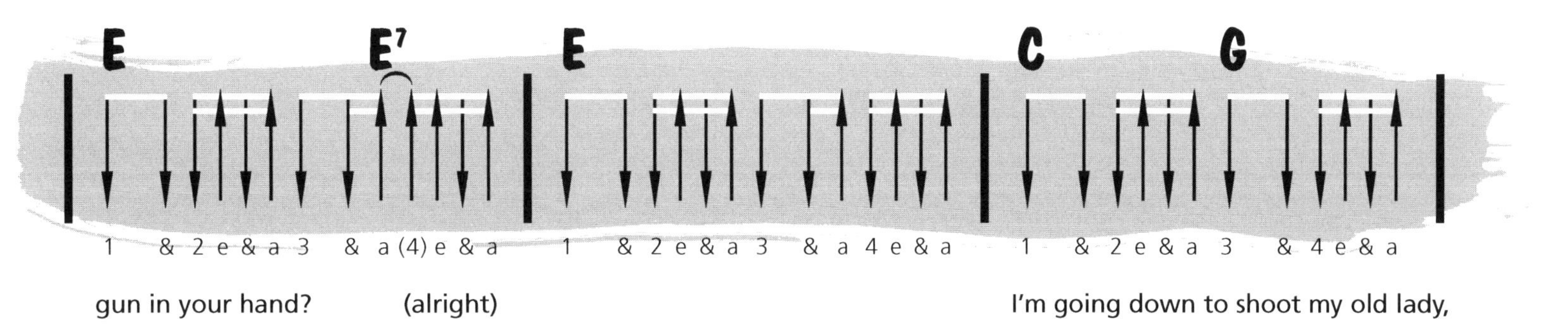
E E7
E
C G
1 & 2 e & a 3 & a (4) e & a
1 & 2 e & a 3 & a 4 e & a
1 & 2 e & a 3 & 4 e & a
gun in your hand? (alright)
I'm going down to shoot my old lady,

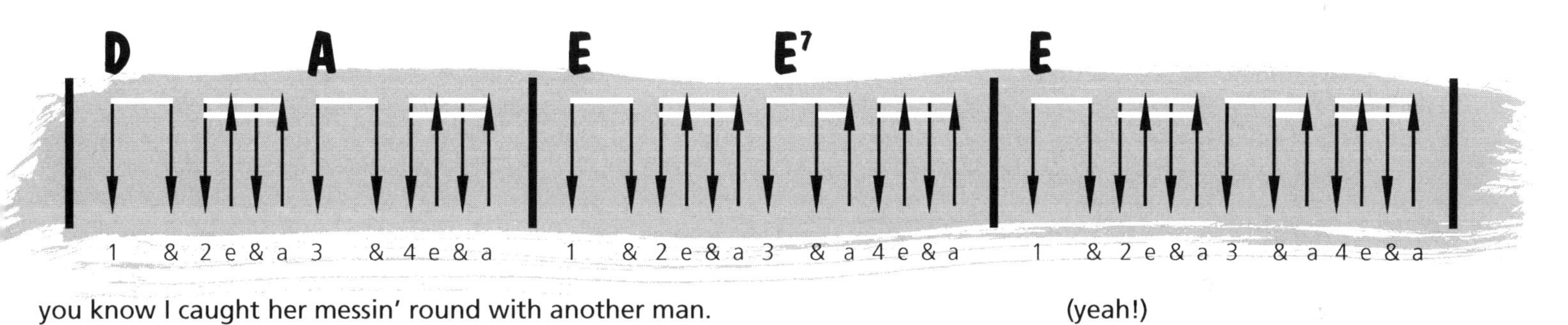
D A
E E7
E
1 & 2 e & a 3 & 4 e & a
1 & 2 e & a 3 & a 4 e & a
1 & 2 e & a 3 & a 4 e & a
you know I caught her messin' round with another man.
(yeah!)

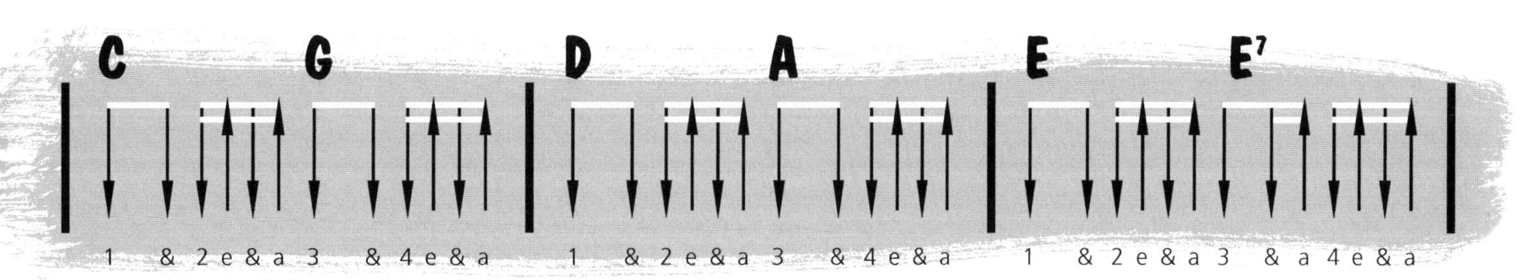
C G
D A
E E7
1 & 2 e & a 3 & 4 e & a
1 & 2 e & a 3 & 4 e & a
1 & 2 e & a 3 & a 4 e & a
I'm going down to shoot my old lady, you know I caught her messin' round with another man. Huh! And that ain't

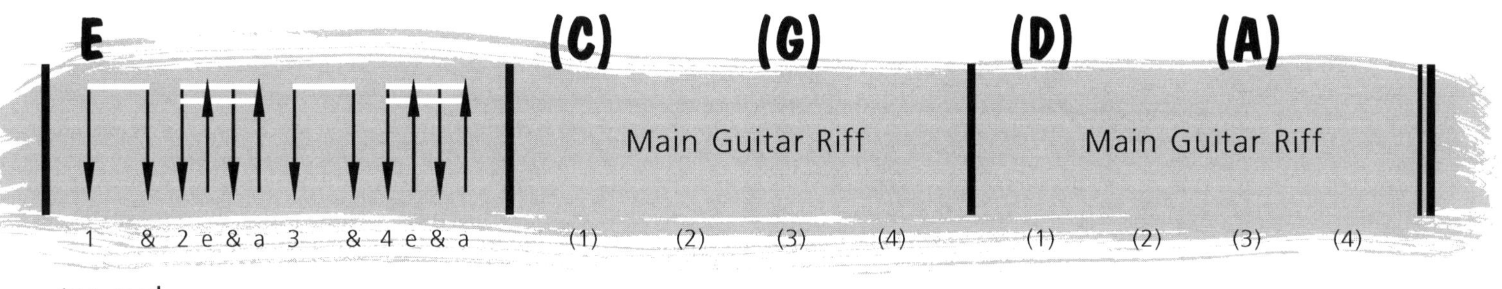
E
(C) (G)
(D) (A)
Main Guitar Riff
Main Guitar Riff
1 & 2 e & a 3 & 4 e & a
(1) (2) (3) (4)
(1) (2) (3) (4)
too cool.

Free

ALL RIGHT NOW

Words & Music by Paul Rodgers & Andy Fraser

Dadd9 Chord

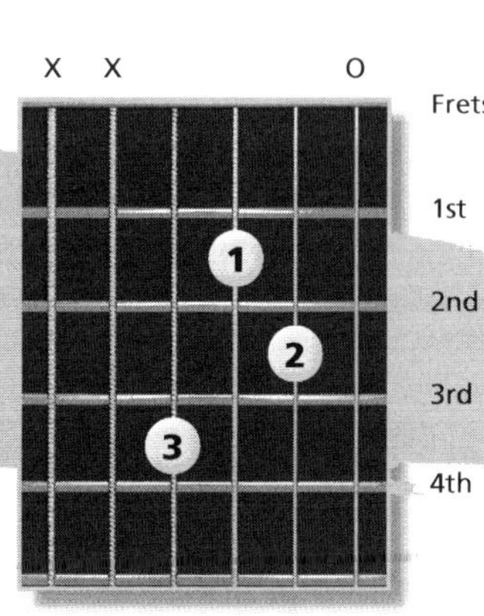

Rock songs don't come much bigger than Free's 'All Right Now', a hit in 1970, 1973 and 1991. Although the song only uses three basic chords - A, D and G, variations on these chords are needed to make what you play sound closer to the original.

Don't worry if you happen to hit the open **A** string under the **Dadd9** chord, it will sound okay. To make the **Dadd9/A** chord, simply strum from the A string instead of from the D.

These chord shapes are suitable for strumming on an acoustic. In the verse there are a number of beats where you need to damp the strings altogether when you hit them (these are beats marked with a 'x'). Watch out for the 'anticipated' chords in the chorus, played on the last offbeat of the bar and tied across into the next bar.

On the second time you play the chorus, watch out for the final A chord – the timing is different. You need to play it on beat 1 of the last bar, rather than beat 4 of the previous bar, so it doesn't sound 'anticipated'.

If you want to try the verse and chorus riffs as they are played on electric guitar, here they are in TAB:

VERSE & INTRO RIFF

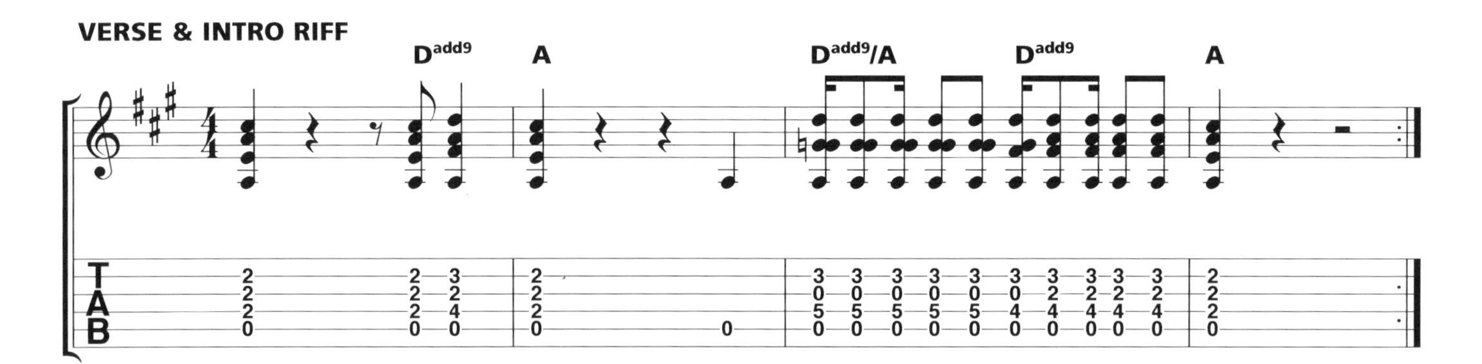

CHORUS RIFF

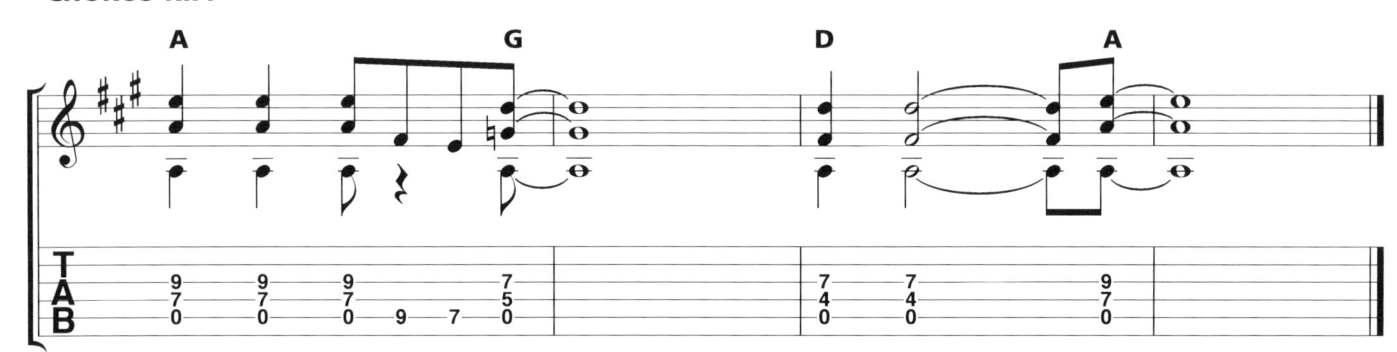

2 BAR CLICK + 8 BAR INTRO
(SEE VERSE & INTRO RIFF)

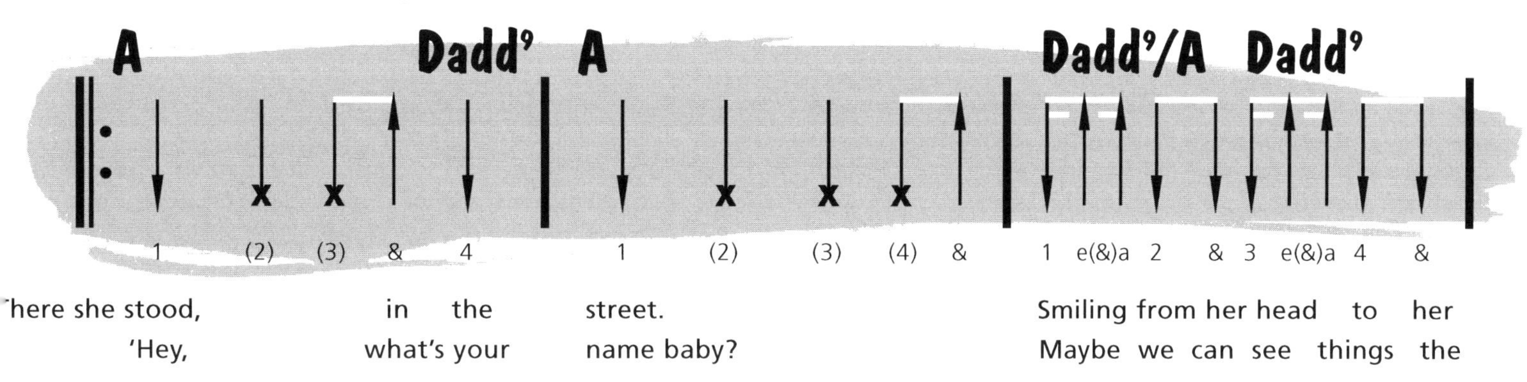

'here she stood, in the street. Smiling from her head to her
'Hey, what's your name baby? Maybe we can see things the

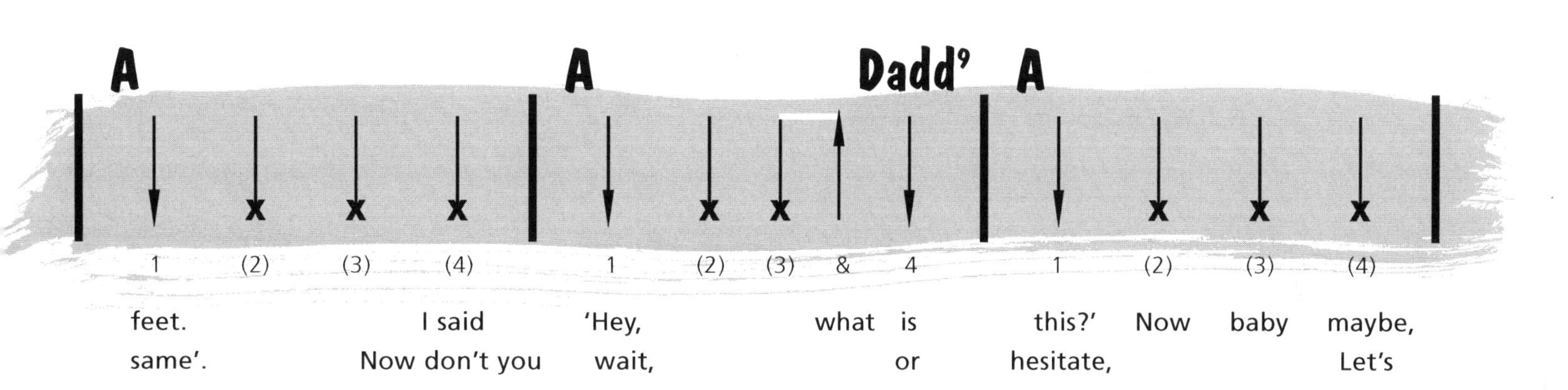

feet. I said 'Hey, what is this?' Now baby maybe,
same'. Now don't you wait, or hesitate, Let's

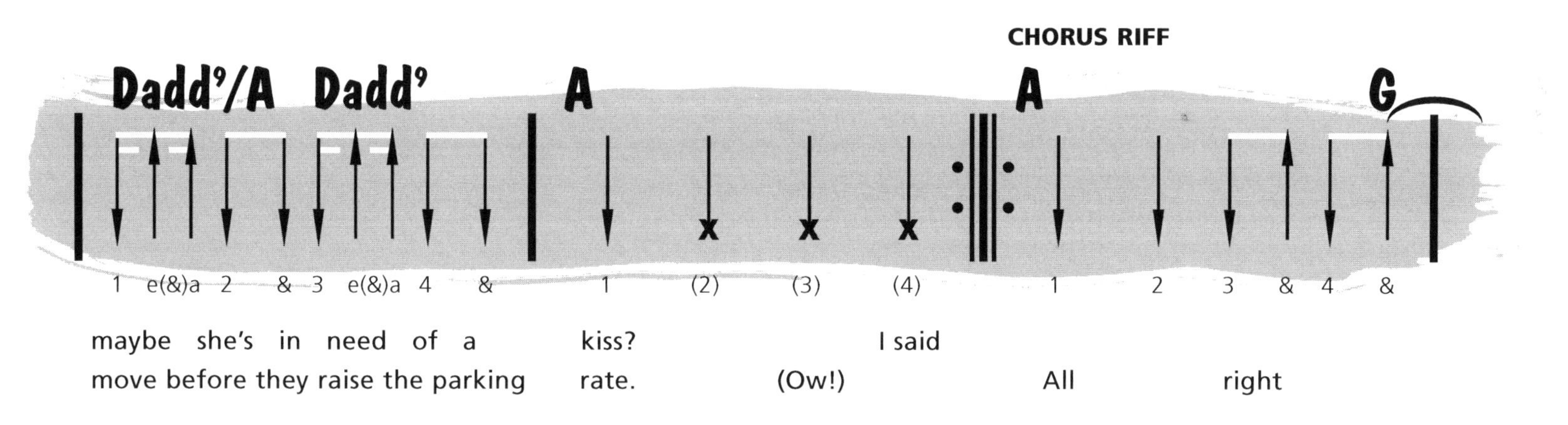

maybe she's in need of a kiss? I said
move before they raise the parking rate. (Ow!) All right

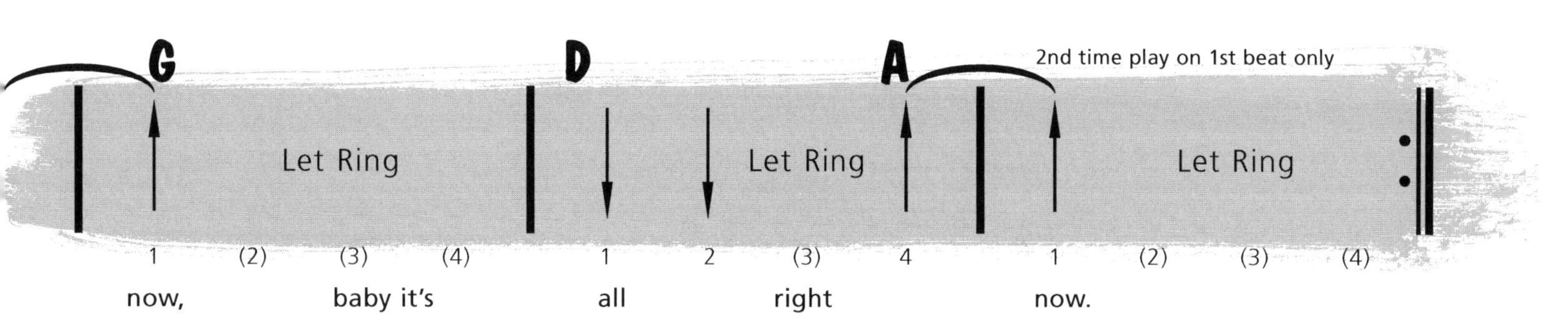

now, baby it's all right now.

NIGHTS IN WHITE SATIN

Words & Music by Justin Hayward

The Moody Blues

Taken from their concept album *Days Of Future Passed*, this romantic ballad charted for The Moody Blues on no less than three occasions, in 1967, 1972 and 1979, and uses a new time-signature: 6/8.

This basically means that there are six quavers in each bar, as opposed to the four crotchets you are used to. 6/8 has a kind of lilting rhythm and is commonly used for ballads.

If you're wondering what the difference is between 6/8 and 3/4 (as they both basically add up to the same number of beats), it is simply that you can 'feel' **two** main beats in each bar of 6/8 (each beat made up of three quavers), whereas in 3/4 it is definitely **three** main beats (each beat made up of two quavers). It is a subtle difference but see if you can spot it.

For more on time signatures, see page 38.

When you have mastered the chord changes and strumming pattern for this song, why not try learning the flute solo as well? We've arranged it for guitar, below:

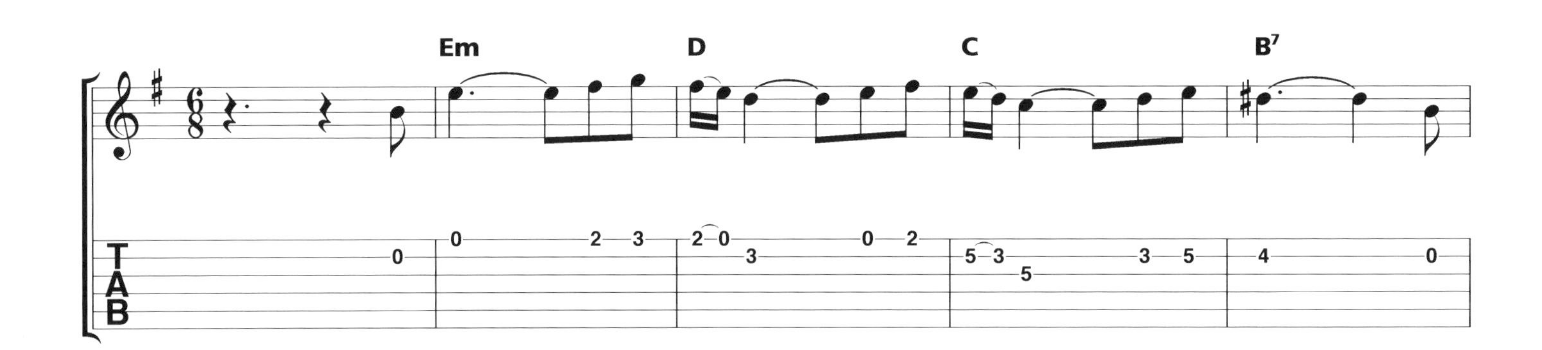

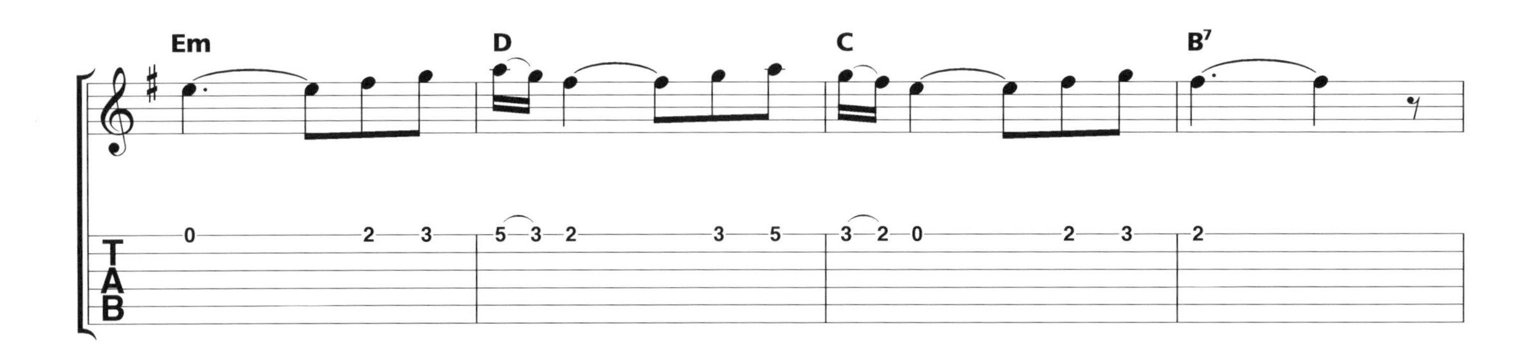

CAPO 3RD FRET
2 BAR CLICK + 4 BAR INTRO

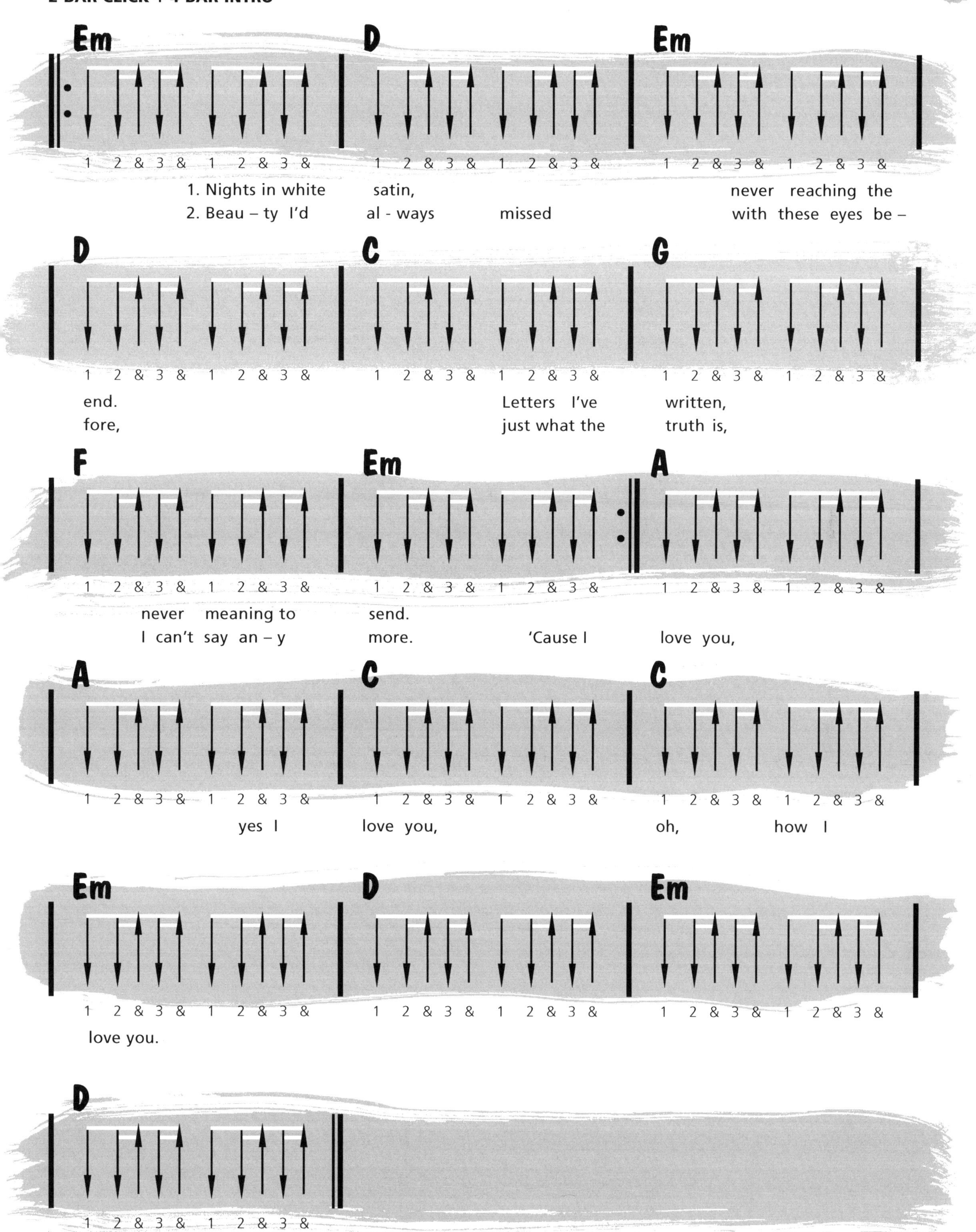

TRACK 28+29

WHILE MY GUITAR GENTLY WEEPS

Words & Music by George Harrison

George Harrison

Am/G Chord

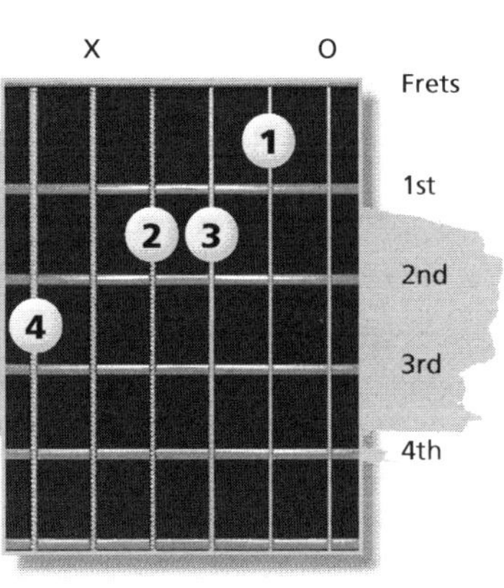

F♯m Chord

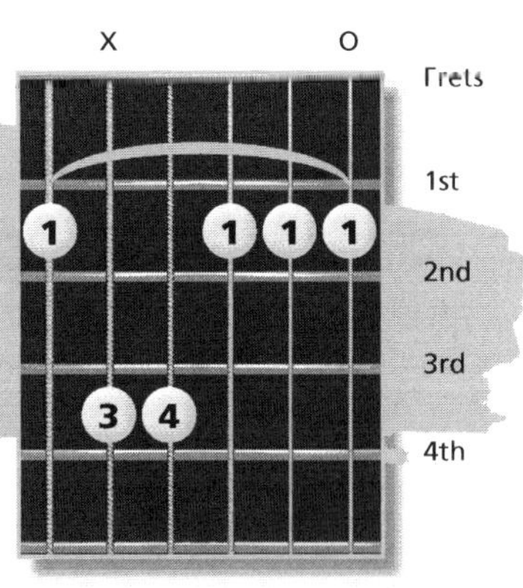

George Harrison's ballad appeared on The Beatles' *White Album*. It introduces one new chord: Am/G.

We could use an **Am7** for this (try it for contrast) but **Am/G** is preferable because it preserves the descending bass line under the chords. The next chord **D/F♯** has that bass-line moving down one more semitone. The **F♯m** in the bridge is an Fm shape moved up one fret.

The strumming is straight 8ths in the verse, but watch out for the tied 2nd offbeat in the Bridge.

This Bridge also happens to be in a different key. The song starts in **A minor** but changes into **A major**. This is why the mood seems to change at that point.

8 BAR INTRO
VERSE

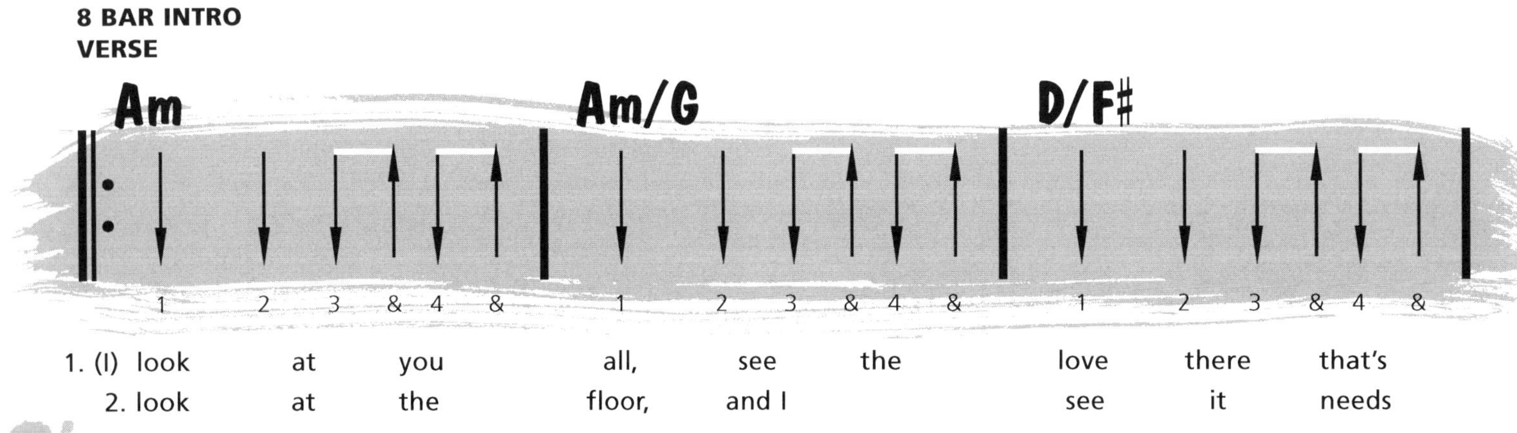

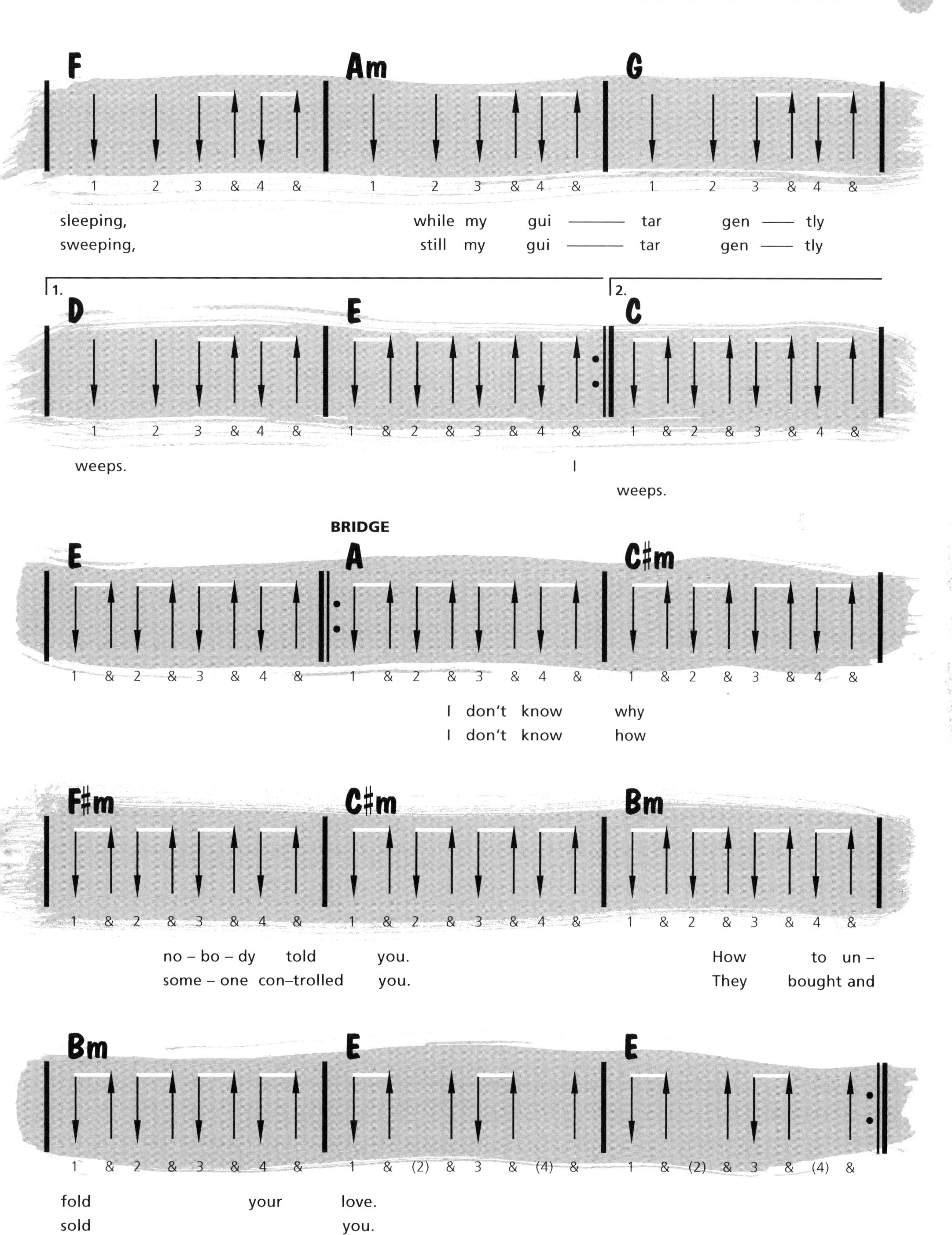
F
Am
G
1 2 3 & 4 & 1 2 3 & 4 & 1 2 3 & 4 &
sleeping, while my gui — tar gen — tly
sweeping, still my gui — tar gen — tly
1.
D
E
2.
C
1 2 3 & 4 & 1 & 2 & 3 & 4 & 1 & 2 & 3 & 4 &
weeps. I
weeps.
BRIDGE
E
A
C♯m
1 & 2 & 3 & 4 & 1 & 2 & 3 & 4 & 1 & 2 & 3 & 4 &
I don't know why
I don't know how
F♯m
C♯m
Bm
1 & 2 & 3 & 4 & 1 & 2 & 3 & 4 & 1 & 2 & 3 & 4 &
no – bo – dy told you. How to un –
some – one con–trolled you. They bought and
Bm
E
E
1 & 2 & 3 & 4 & 1 & (2) & 3 & (4) & 1 & (2) & 3 & (4) &
fold your love.
sold you.

PINBALL WIZARD

Words & Music by Pete Townshend

This hit by The Who comes from their rock opera *Tommy*.

You are already familiar with **sus4** chords, but for this song, we're going to have to take it up a few frets, to the 7th. Look at the chord on the right – **Bsus4/B***. Start with a partial barre at the seventh fret, using your first finger. To get the bass note, you'll need to use your thumb too – a tricky technique that might need some practice. You also need to mute the fifth string with the side of your thumb. Then place your other fingers down. Now, strum fast while adding and removing your little finger at the 9th fret – and you've got the intro to 'Pinball Wizard'!

The strum is also challenging, as it's so fast and also accented in an unusual way. Listen to the CD first, then take a look at the music. See if you can 'feel' where the accents should fall. Alternatively, try counting this rhythm accenting the **1** and not counting the (&):

1 2 3 **1** 2 3 **1** 2 3 **1** 2 3 **1** (&) **2** (&)

Now you've almost got it, but there's also the famous intro to learn. We've written it out in TAB, below. Use down strokes to keep the 8th note **F♯** going, playing the chord only once, on the first beat of the bar.

Bsus4/B* Chord

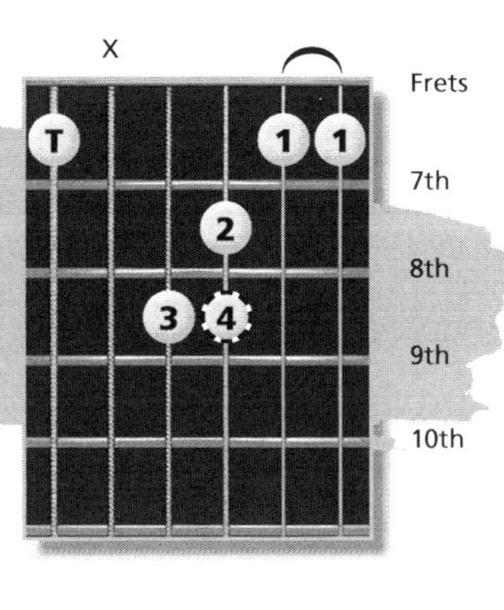

Dsus4 Chord

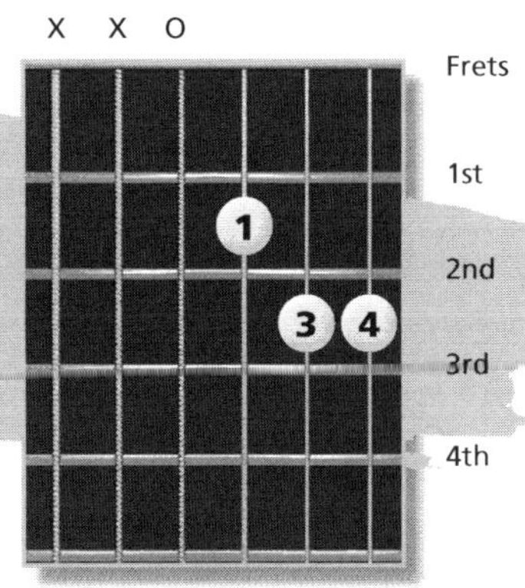

Bmajor Chord

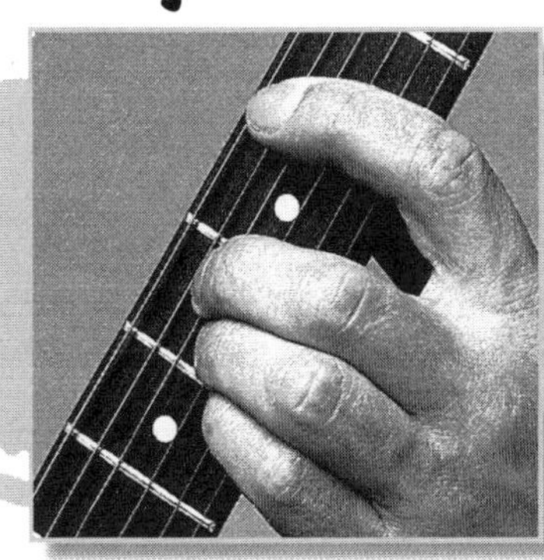

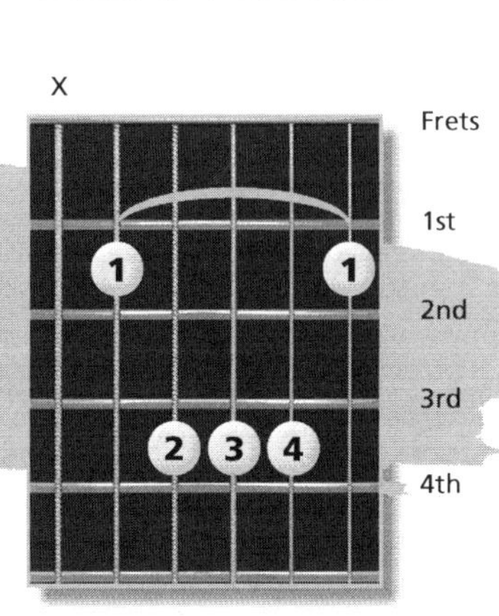

2 BAR CLICK INTRO

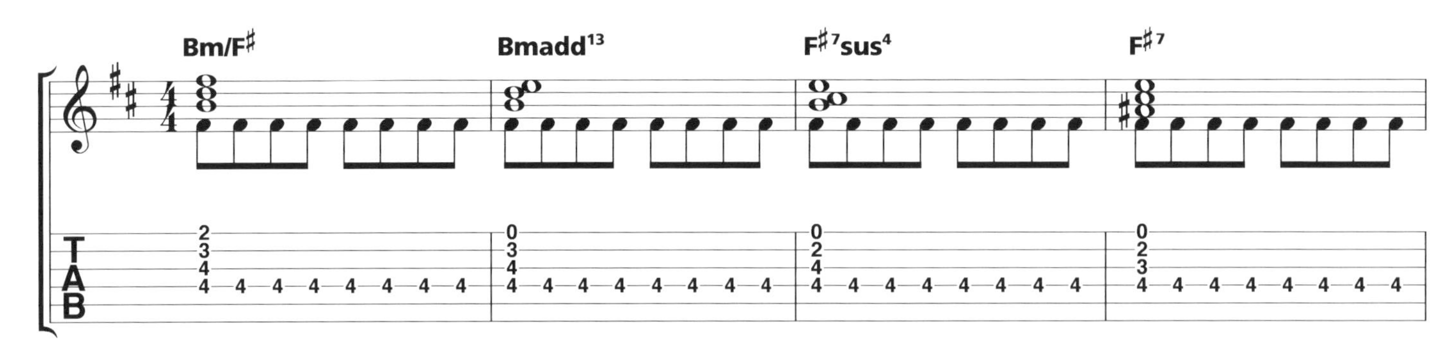

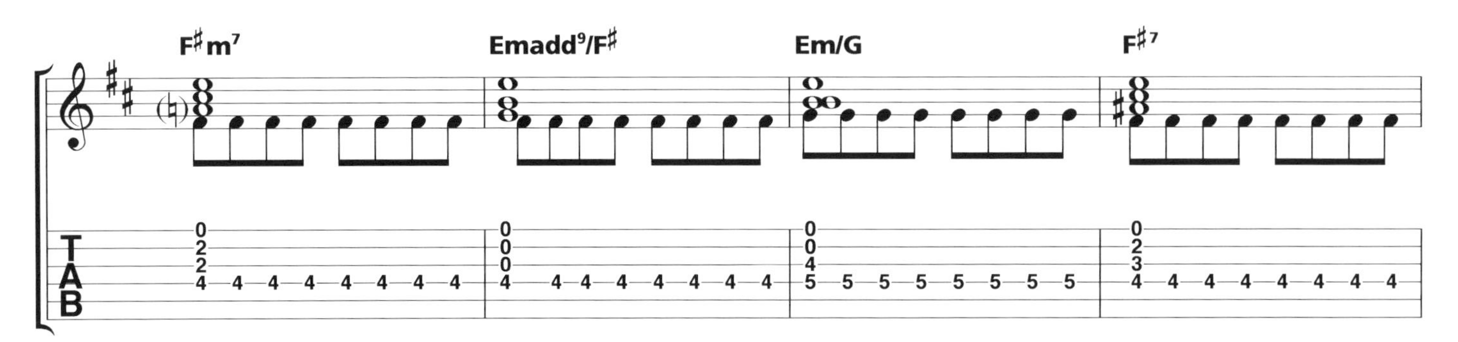

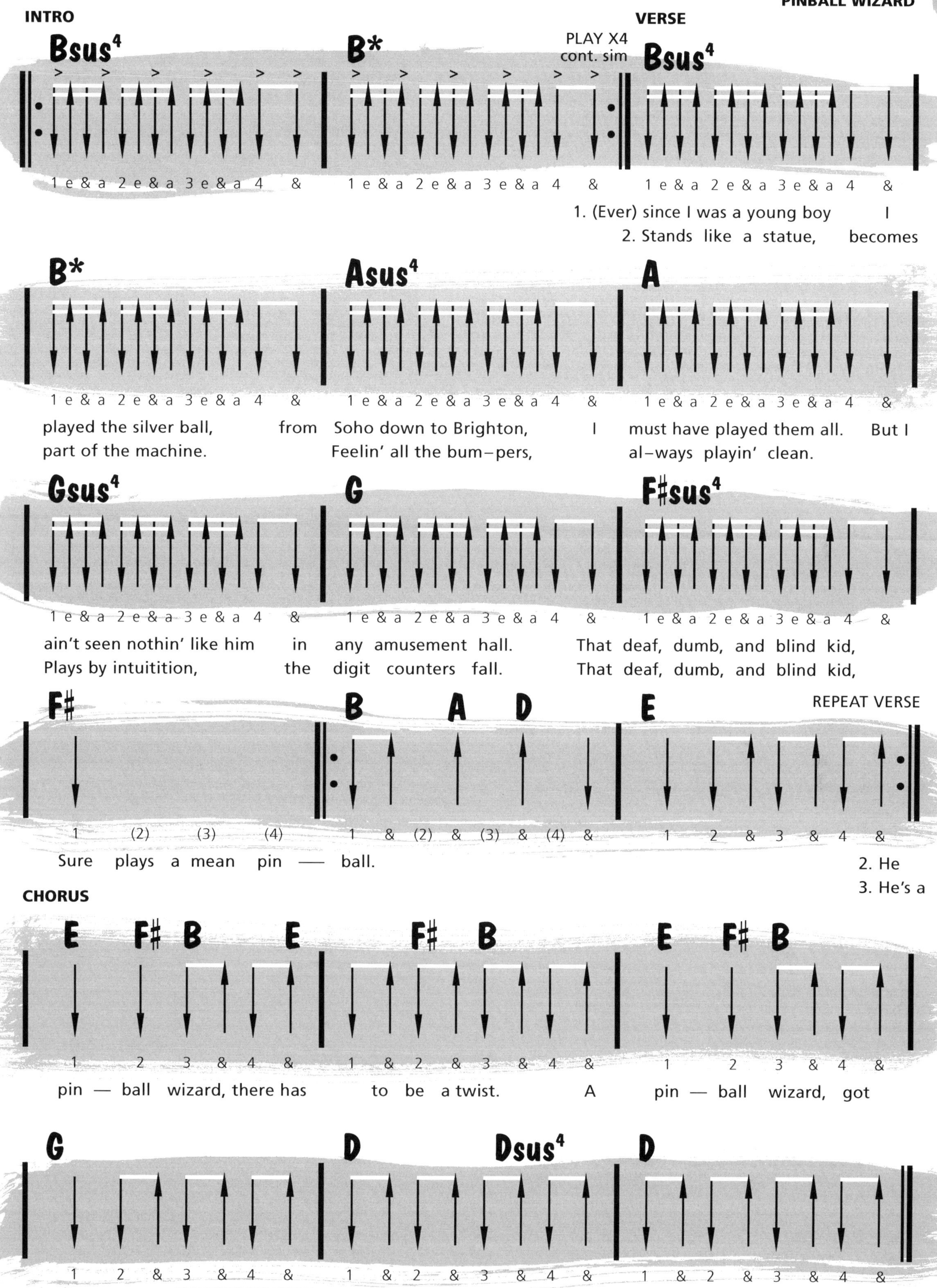
INTRO
Bsus4
B*
PLAY X4
cont. sim
VERSE
Bsus4
1 e & a 2 e & a 3 e & a 4 &
1. (Ever) since I was a young boy I
2. Stands like a statue, becomes
B*
Asus4
A
played the silver ball, from Soho down to Brighton, I must have played them all. But I
part of the machine. Feelin' all the bum–pers, al–ways playin' clean.
Gsus4
G
F♯sus4
ain't seen nothin' like him in any amusement hall. That deaf, dumb, and blind kid,
Plays by intuitition, the digit counters fall. That deaf, dumb, and blind kid,
F♯
B A D
E
REPEAT VERSE
1 (2) (3) (4)
1 & (2) & (3) & (4) &
1 2 & 3 & 4 &
Sure plays a mean pin — ball.
2. He
3. He's a
CHORUS
E F♯ B E
F♯ B
E F♯ B
1 2 3 & 4 &
1 & 2 & 3 & 4 &
pin — ball wizard, there has to be a twist. A pin — ball wizard, got
G
D Dsus4
D
such a sup – ple wrist.

LIGHT MY FIRE

Words & Music by Jim Morrison, Robbie Krieger, Ray Manzarek & John Densmore

Jim Morrison

This great song has been a hit for several performers. The most famous was the original version by The Doors with Jim Morrison on vocals, which charted in 1967 and 1991. Jose Feliciano had a bigger hit with the song in 1968.

When practising minor sevenths play a straight minor version of the chord first, followed by the minor seventh, and listen to the subtle difference in sound.

The **Am7** is simple and needs no explanation, but for the **F♯m7** refer to the **F♯m** shape introduced in '**While My Guitar Gently Weeps**'. Take your little finger off the fourth string. As long as you're careful that your barre (first finger) is pressing down cleanly across the strings you should now be playing **F♯m7**. As this **F♯m7** shape does not use any open strings it is 'moveable'. These two shapes both take their name from the note you are fingering on the sixth string.

That is to say, if:
The tip of your 1st finger is resting on the 2nd fret of the 6th string, the chord is **F♯m7**.

The tip of your 1st finger is resting on the 3rd fret of the 6th string, the chord is **Gm7**.

The tip of your 1st finger is resting on the 4th fret of the 6th string, the chord is **G♯m7**.

Here in TAB is the organ introduction melody.

This is quite fast, so take your time playing it slowly at first and make sure you are using all four fingers to fret these notes.

2 BAR CLICK

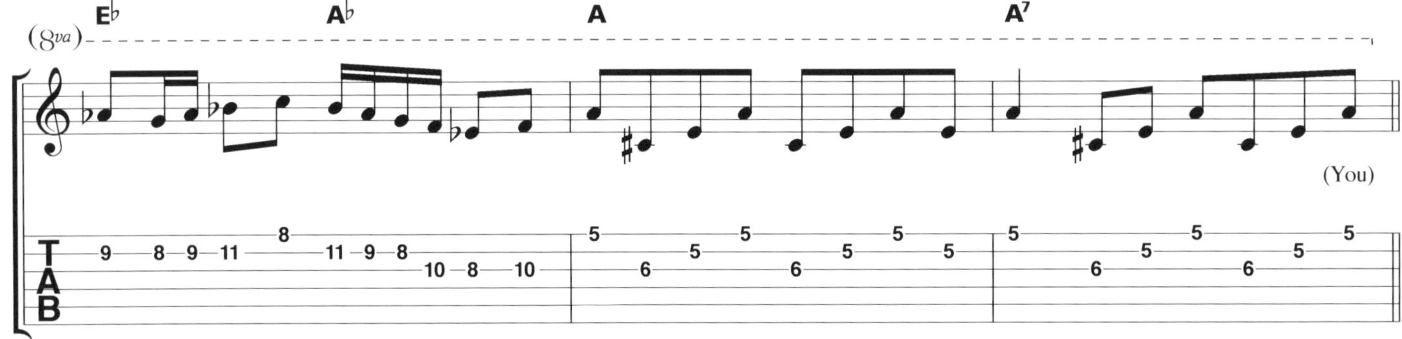

2 BAR CLICK + 5 BAR INTRO
VERSE

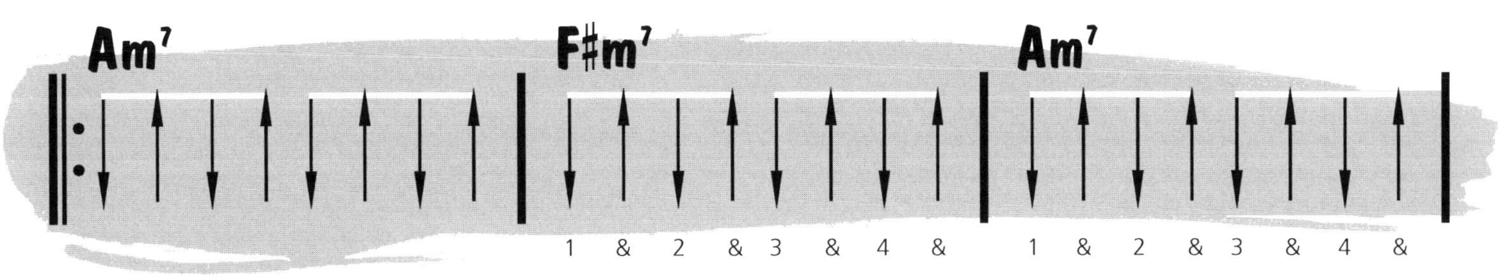

1. (You) know that it would be un – true, you know that I would be a li – ar,
time to hes – it – ate is through, no time to wallow in the myre.

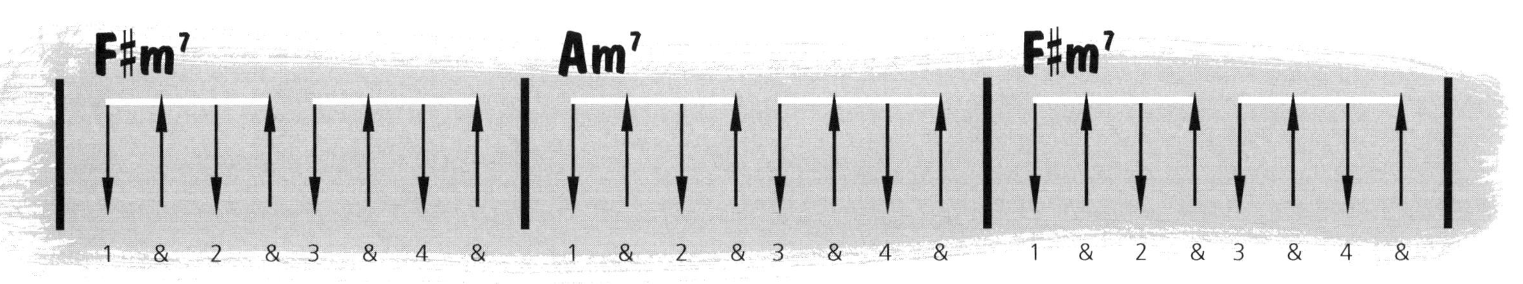

If I was to say to you.
Try now, we can on – ly lose. And our

CHORUS

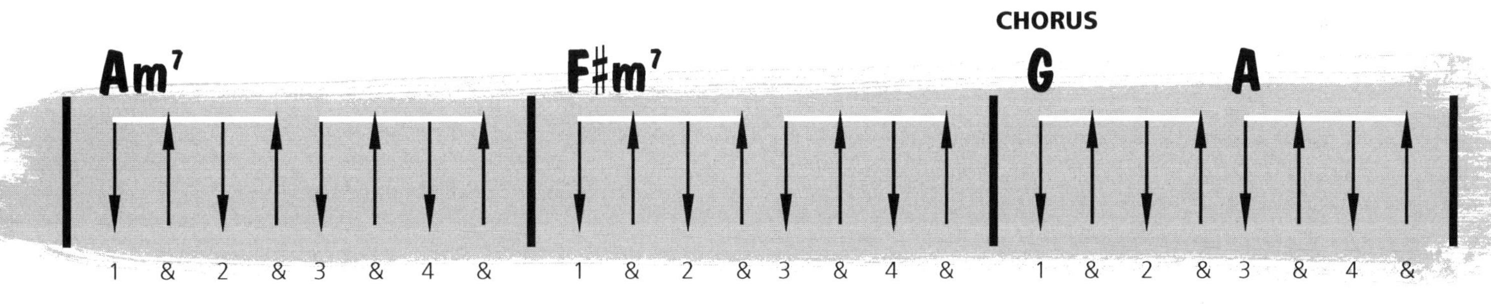

Girl, we couldn't get much higher. Come on ba – by, light my fire.
love become a funeral pyre.

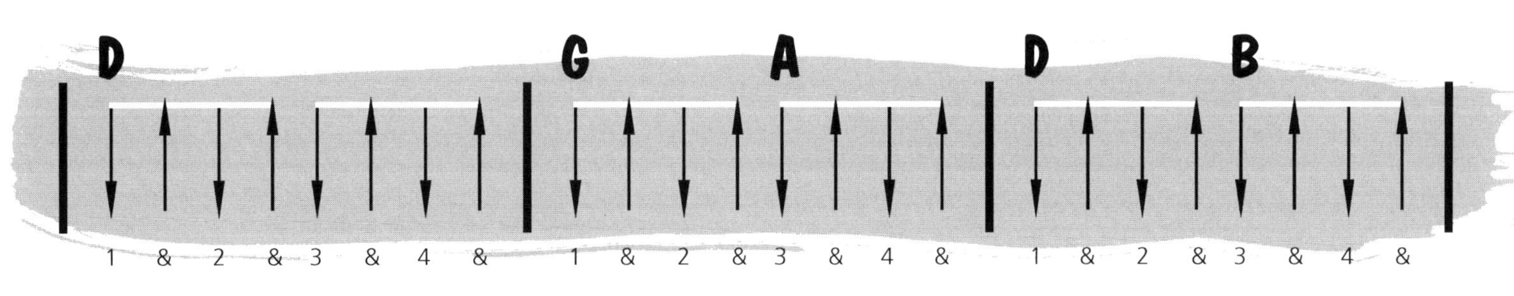

Come on ba – by, light my fire.

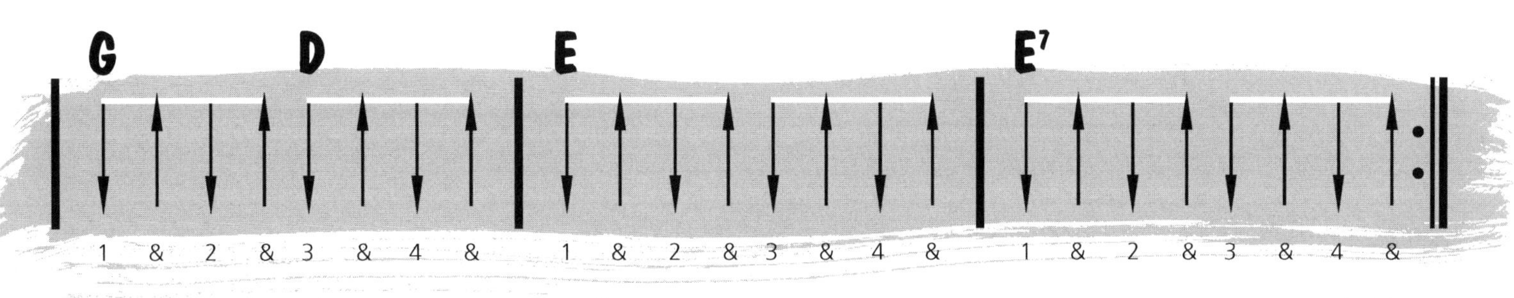

Try to set the night on fire. 2. The

READING MUSIC MADE EASY

THE STAVE

The music we play is written on five equally spaced lines called a **stave** or staff.

Staves are divided into **bars** (or measures) by the use of a vertical line.

Each bar has a fixed number of **beats** in it. A beat is the natural tapping rhythm of a song. Most songs have four beats in each bar, and we can tap our feet or count along with these songs.

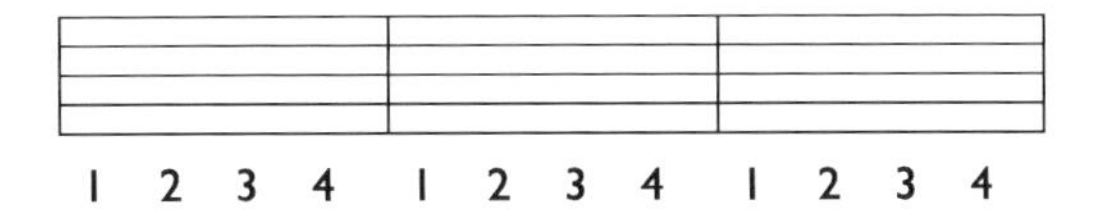

Occasionally, there are three beats in each bar, and we count like this:

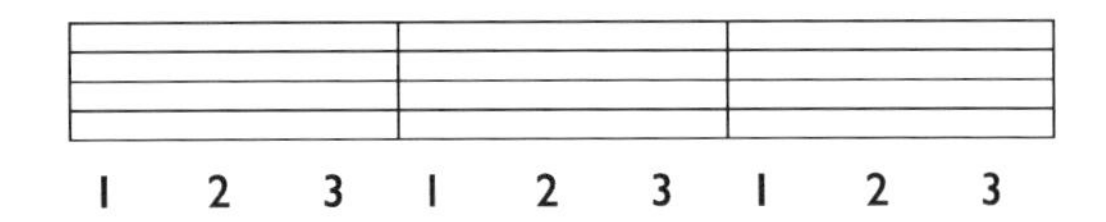

TIME SIGNATURES

At the beginning of every piece of music there are two numbers, written one above the other. This is called a **time signature**. The top number tells us how many beats are in a bar. The lower number tells us the value of these beats as expressed in the musical notation (this will be explained shortly).

The two most common time signatures in popular music are these:

4/4 is often shown as C, or **Common Time**.

Once given, the time signature is not repeated, unless the beat changes within a song. This happens only rarely in popular music.

CLEFS

The other symbol we find at the beginning of each stave is called the **treble clef**.

This fixes the pitch of the notes on the stave.
The line that passes through the centre of the spiral, second up from the bottom, fixes the note G.
We will look more at notes and pitch in a moment.

FORM NOTATION (REPEAT SIGNS)

In music there are various standard markings which can be used to abbreviate the layout. When we come to this sign:

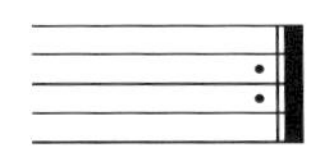

it tells us to go back to where this sign appears:

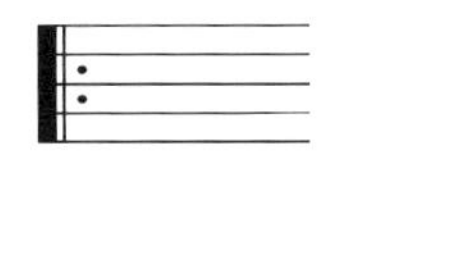

(or sometimes when this does not appear, we return to the beginning) and **repeat** the section.

1ST & 2ND TIME BARS

Sometimes we repeat the whole section, but the ending of the 'second time through' can be different from the first time. Thus we have what are called **1st** and **2nd** time bars (or a 3rd and 4th for that matter.)
Here is an example:

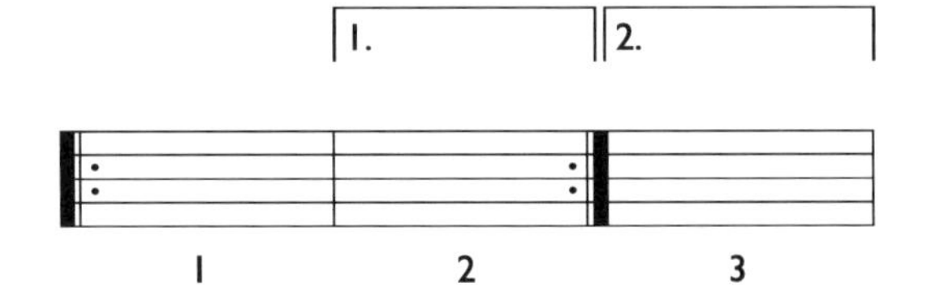

The first time through we play bars 1 and 2.
The second time we play bars 1 and 3.

D.C. & D.S.

We often see the letters D.C. and D.S. at the end of a stave line. D.C. (from the Italian ***da capo***) tells us to return to the beginning ('top'). D.S. (***dal segno***) means return to the sign (𝄋). After these letters we see the words al coda (**to the coda**) or al fine (to the finish). The coda is the end section of a song, usually short. Here is an example:

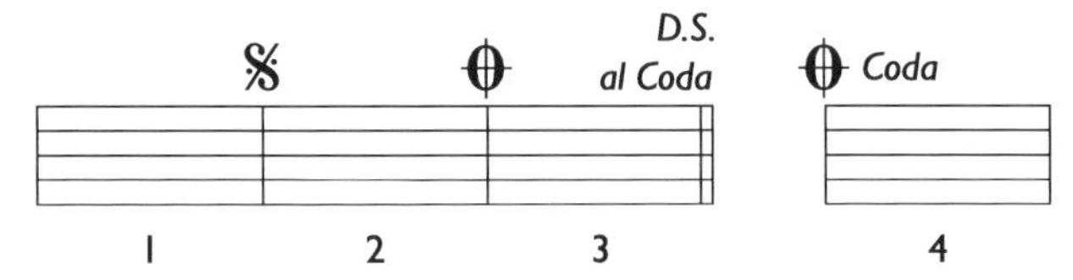

Here we plays bars 1-3. We are then directed back to bar 2, and continue to bar 3, when the sign (𝄌) above the bar line tells us to jump to the coda at bar 4.

Here is another example:

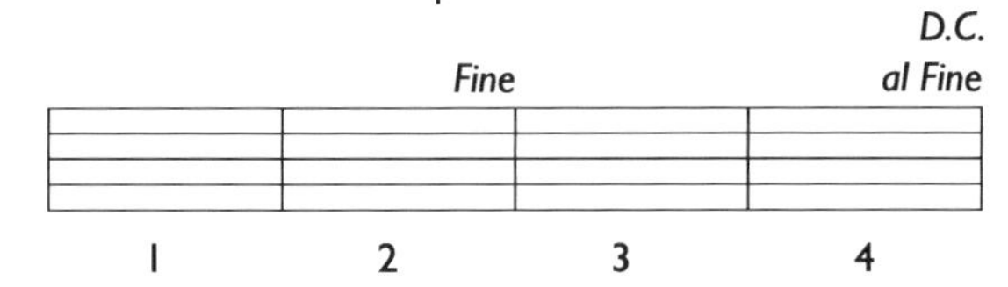

Play bars 1-4. Then return to bar 1, and continue to bar 2, where the word Fine (or end) tells us to stop. Sometimes coupled with the word Fine we see the sign (𝄐) over a chord or note. This means you pause on the beat marked, letting the final chord ring. This is a very common ending.

(𝄎) means that you should repeat the preceding bar.

is played

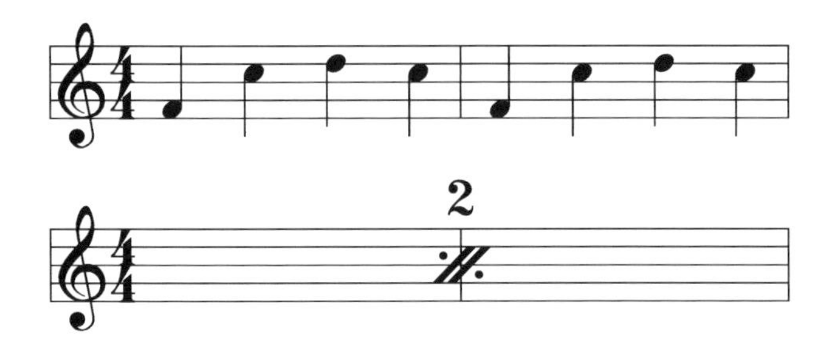

means that you should repeat the preceding two bars.

NOTE VALUES

Now we come to notes and their time values. The notes tell the player exactly what to play, how to play it, and when to play it.

Semibreve (or whole note):

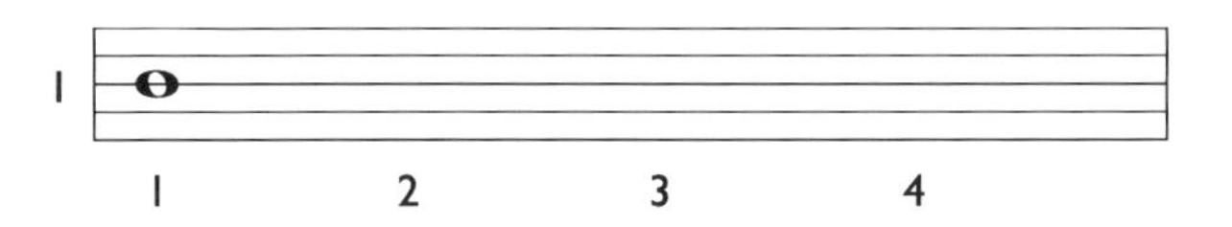

Minim (or half note):

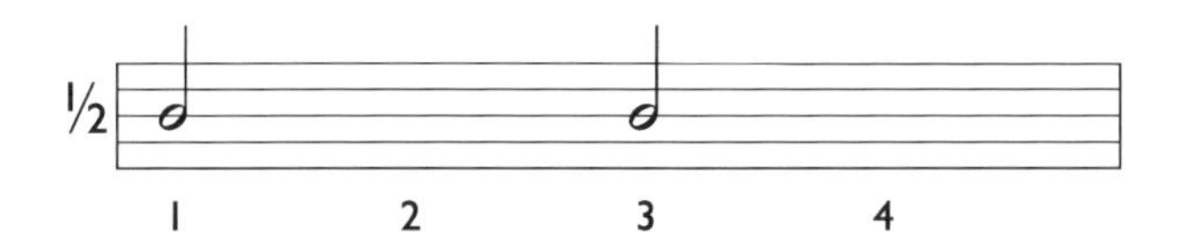

Crotchet (or quarter note):

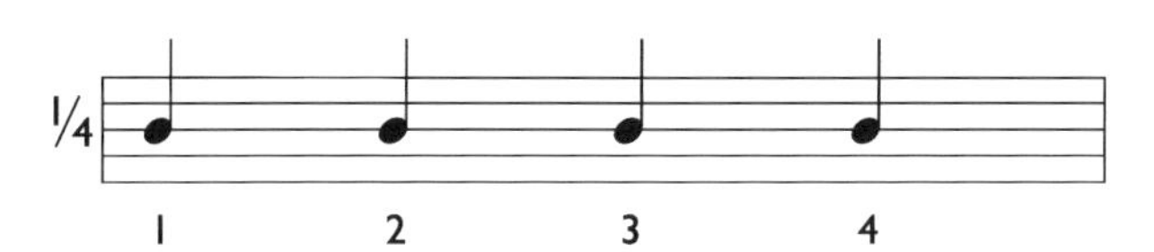

Quaver (or eighth note):

Semiquaver (or sixteenth note):

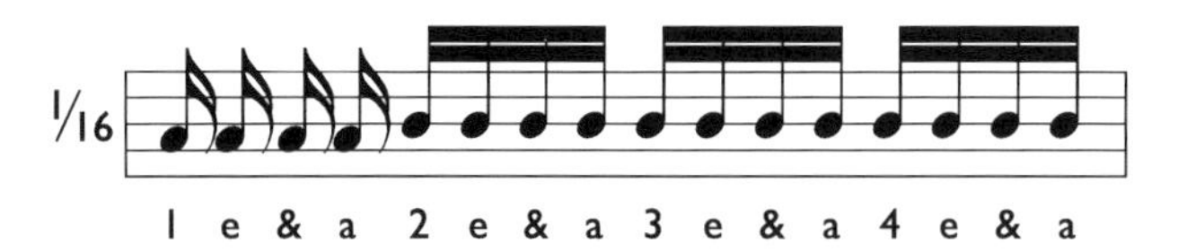

The notes in each diagram all add up to 4 beats, the beat being 1 crotchet. Quavers and semiquavers are joined together with 'beams' to make the music tidier.

So in a piece of music in 4/4 time we count 4 beats to the bar, each beat being 1 crotchet:

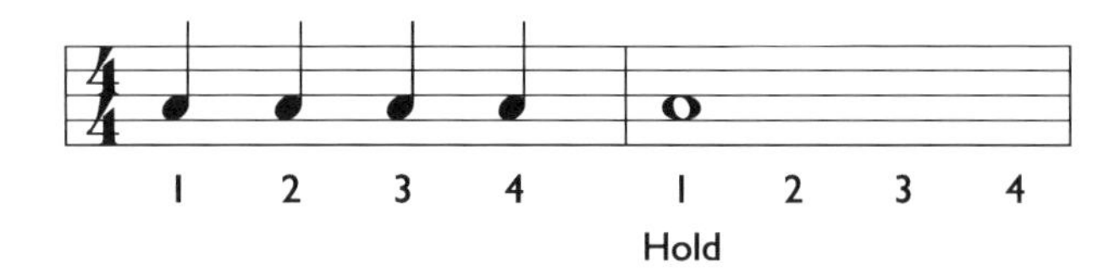

A bar in 2/4 time will contain 2 crotchet beats per bar:

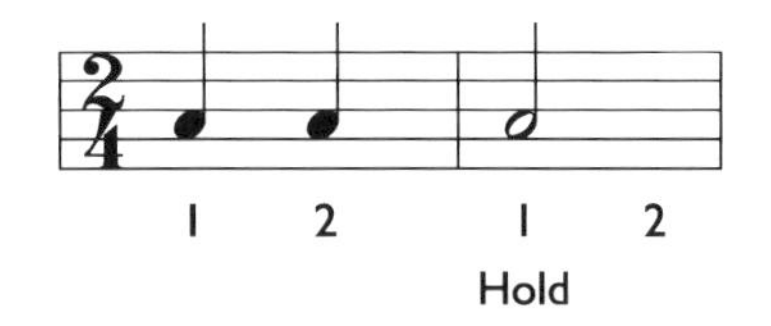

The same principle applies to 3/4 time:

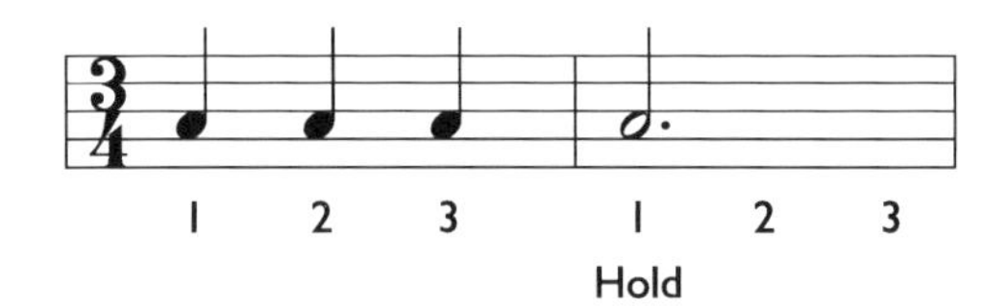

DOTTED NOTES

Above, we see a minim with a **dot** after it.
The dot increases the time value of any note after which it is placed by half.

So, a **dotted minim**: 2 beats + 1 beat = 3 beats.

A **dotted crotchet**: $1 + {}^{1}/_{2} = 1\,{}^{1}/_{2}$ beats.

COUNTING

Many guitar accompaniments consist of strumming 8 quavers to each bar of 4/4 time. We still count 4 crotchets but to maintain an easy rhythm we count 1 & 2 & 3 & 4 &, each syllable being one quaver:

We can break this counting down further, so with semiquaver rhythms the count would be: 1e&a 2e&a 3e&a 4e&a, each syllable being one semiquaver:

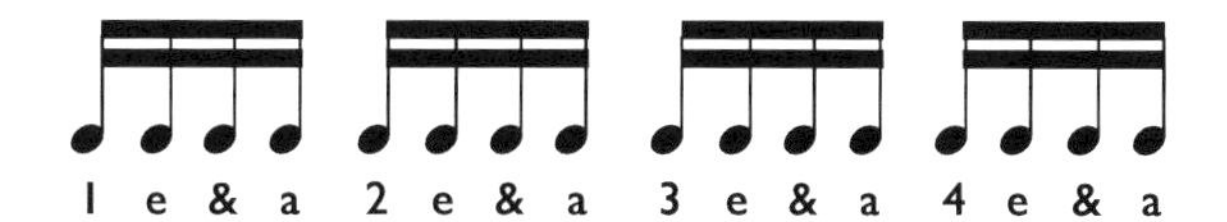

Sometimes we see dotted quavers and semiquavers joined together. Again we count four, but the rhythm does not flow smoothly as with 8 quavers to the bar, and we count like this:

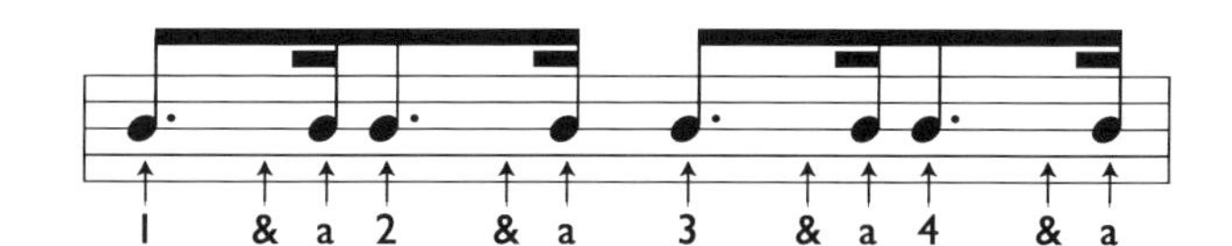

RESTS

Just as notes tell us when to play, we have **rests** which tell us when not to play. There is a rest which corresponds in value to each type of note.

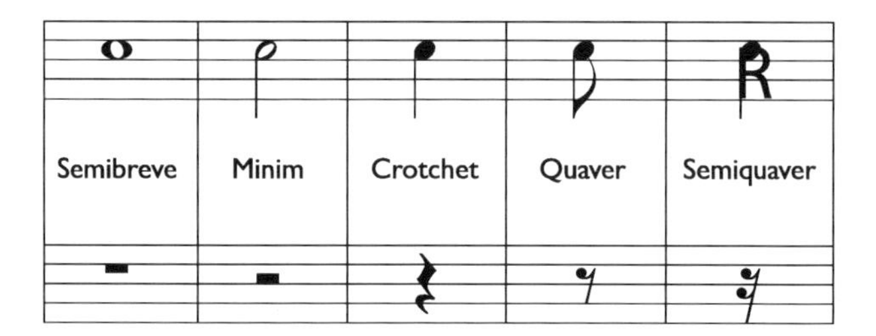

Similarly, dotted rests have the same time values as dotted notes.

A whole bar's rest is generally shown by a semibreve rest, whether or not the music is in 4/4 time.

PITCH

Here is the scale of **C major**.

A **tone** (T) is made up of **2 semitones** (S/T) and semitones correspond to the **frets** on your guitar, i.e. **C** to **D** is a tone or two frets, and **E** to **F** is a semitone or one fret.

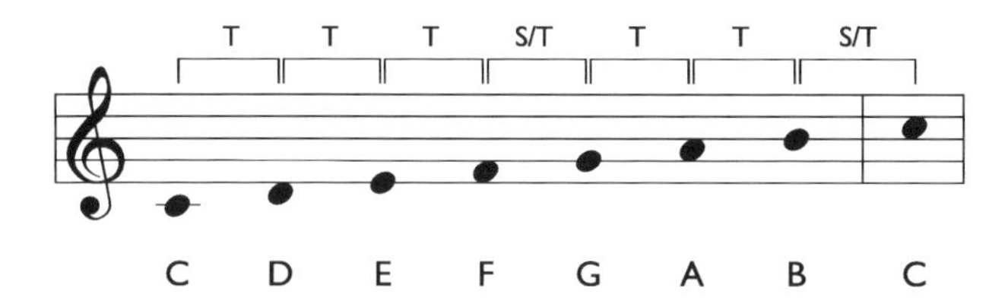

This is an octave and can be repeated up or down the stave.

LEGER LINES

The first C is below the stave and we see that a **leger** line runs through the note. This is an extension of the stave to accommodate the note. Here are more examples:

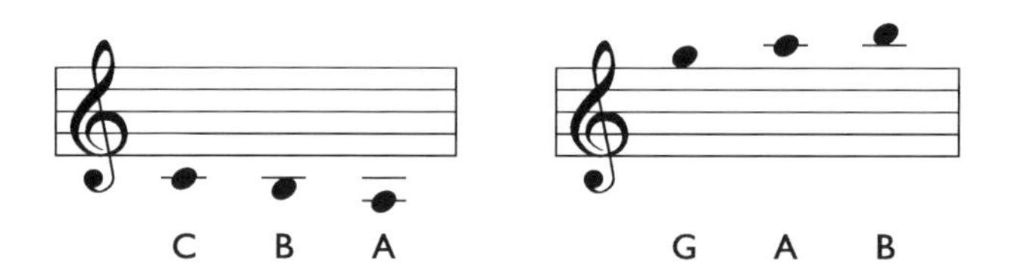

KEY SIGNATURE

At the beginning of each stave line we see, after the treble clef, the **key signature** of the music. This consists of sharps or flats or, in the case of C major or A minor none at all, and indicates that all notes against which they are set should be raised or lowered by a **semitone**.

Here, all **F**s are to be raised by a semitone in all octaves.

Here, all **B**s and **E**s are to be lowered by a semitone in all octaves:

ACCIDENTALS

It is necessary sometimes to insert **sharps** or **flats** that do not occur in the key signature. They are called **accidentals**. In this case we put the sign before the individual note, and its effect lasts for one bar only. The **natural** sign (♮) is also used to countermand a sharp or flat given in the key signature.
Again its effect is for one bar only:

TIES

Finally we come to the curved line called a **tie**, which, in its various functions, will occur in these books.

It has the effect of joining together two notes. When you see two notes of the same pitch tied together you simply play the first one and let it ring on through the note to which it is tied.

These are the basic outlines of reading and understanding written music.

ADDITIONAL LYRICS

BLUE SUEDE SHOES

Verse 1
Well it's one for the money
Two for the show
Three to get ready, now go, cat, go...
But don't you step on my blue
suede shoes.
You can do anything but stay off
of my blue suede shoes.

Verse 2
Well you can knock me down
Step on my face
Slander my name all over the place
Do anything that you want to do
But ah-ah honey lay off of them
shoes...
And don't you step on my blue
suede shoes.
You can do anything but stay off
of my blue suede shoes.

Let's go cats!

Verse 3
You can burn my house, steal my car
Drink my liquor from an old fruit jar
Well do anything that you want to do
But ah-ah honey lay off of my shoes...
And don't you step on my blue
suede shoes.
You can do anything but stay off of
my blue suede shoes.

Verse 4
Well it's one for the money
Two for the show
Three to get ready, now go, go, go...
But don't you step on my blue
suede shoes.
You can do anything but stay off
of my blue suede shoes.

Coda
Well it's blue, blue, blue suede shoes
Blue, blue, blue suede shoes, yeah!
Blue, blue, blue suede shoes, baby!
Blue, blue, blue suede shoes
Well you can do anything but stay off
of my blue suede shoes.

DRIFTWOOD

Verse 1
Everything is open
Nothing is set in stone
Rivers turn to oceans
Oceans tide you home
Home is where the heart is
But your heart had to roam
Drifting over bridges
Never to return
Watching bridges burn.

Chorus
You're driftwood floating underwater
Breaking into pieces, pieces, pieces.
Just driftwood, hollow and of no use
Waterfalls will find you, bind you
Grind you.

Verse 2
Nobody is an island
Everyone has to go
Pillars turn to butter
Butter flying low
Low is where your heart is
But your heart has to grow
Drifting under bridges
Never with the flow.

Bridge
And you really didn't think it would
happen
But it really is the end of the line.

Chorus
So I'm sorry that you've turned
to driftwood
But you've been drifting for a long
long time.

Verse 3
Everywhere there's trouble
Nowhere's safe to go
Pushes turn to shovels
Shovelling the snow
Frozen you have chosen
The path you wish to go
Drifting now forever
And forever more
Until you reach your shore.

Chorus
You're driftwood floating underwater
Breaking into pieces, pieces, pieces.
Just driftwood, hollow and of no use
Waterfalls will find you, bind you
Grind you, and you...

Bridge
Really didn't think it would happen
But it really is the end of the line.

Chorus
So I'm sorry that you've turned
to driftwood
But you've been drifting for a long
long time
You've been drifting for a long, long
time
You've been drifting for a long, long
Drifting for a long, long time.

SAIL AWAY

Chorus
Sail away with me honey
I put my heart in your hands
Sail away with me honey now
Now, now.
Sail away with me
What will be will be
I wanna hold you now, now, now.

Verse 2
Crazy skies all wild above me now
Winter howling at my face
And everything I held so dear
Disappeared without a trace
Oh all the times I've tasted love
Never knew quite what I had
Little darling if you hear me now
Never needed you so bad
Spinning round inside my head.

Chorus

Verse 2
I've been talking drunken gibberish
Falling in and out of bars
Trying to get some explanation here
For the way some people are.
How did it ever come so far?

Repeat Chorus x 2

Verse 3
Sail away with me honey
I put my heart in your hands
You'll break me up if you put me
down, whoa———.
Sail away with me
What will be will be
I wanna hold you now, now, now.

WILD WOOD

Verse 1
High tide, mid-afternoon
People fly by in the traffic's boom
Knowing just where you're blowing
Getting to where
You should be going.

Verse 2
Don't let them get you down
Making you feel guilty about
Golden rain will bring you riches
All the good things you deserve now.

Verse 3
Climbing, forever trying
Find your way out
Of the wild wild wood.
Now there's no justice
You've only yourself
That you can trust in.

Verse 4
And I said, high tide, mid-afternoon
People fly by in the traffic's boom
Knowing just where you're blowing
Getting to where
You should be going.

Verse 5
Day by day, your world fades away
Waiting to feel all the dreams that say
Golden rain will bring you riches
All the good things you deserve now
And I say...

Verse 6
Climbing, forever trying
You're gonna find your way out
Of the wild, wild wood.
I said, you're gonna find your way out
Of the wild, wild wood.

ROLL WITH IT

Verse 1
You gotta roll with it
You gotta take your time
You gotta say what you say
Don't let anybody get in your way
'Cause it's all too much for me to take.

Verse 2
Don't ever stand aside
Don't ever be denied
You wanna be who you'd be
If you're coming with me.
I think I've got a feeling I've lost
inside
I think I'm gonna take me away
and hide
I'm thinking things that I just can't
abide.

Bridge
I know the roads down which your
life will drive
I find the key that lets you slip inside
Kiss the girl, she's not behind the door
But you know I think I recognise
your face
But I've never seen you before.

Repeat Verse 1

Instrumental

Repeat Bridge

Repeat Verse 1

Coda
Don't ever stand aside
Don't ever be denied
You wanna be who you'd be
If you're coming with me.

I think I've got a feeling I've lost
inside. *(repeat ad lib to fade)*

20TH CENTURY BOY

Verse 1
Friends say it's fine
Friends say it's good
Everybody says it's
Just like Robin Hood.
I move like a cat
Charge like a ram
Sting like a bee, babe!
I wanna be your man.

Chorus
But it's plain to see
You were meant for me, yeah
I'm your boy
Your Twentieth Century toy.

Verse 2
Friends say it's fine
Friends say it's good
Everybody says it's
Just like Robin Hood.
Fly like a plane, drive like a car
Bark like a hound, babe!
I wanna be your man.

Chorus 2
But it's plain to see
You were meant for me, yeah
I'm your toy
Your Twentieth Century boy.

Bridge
Twentieth century toy
I wanna be your boy.
Twentieth century boy
I wanna be your toy.
Twentieth century toy
I wanna be your boy.
Twentieth century boy
I wanna be your toy.

Repeat Verse 1

Repeat Chorus

Repeat Bridge

SHE LOVES YOU

Intro
She loves you, yeah, yeah, yeah
She loves you, yeah, yeah, yeah
She loves you, yeah, yeah, yeah, yeah.

Verse 1
You think you've lost your love
Well I saw her yesterday
It's you she's thinking of
And she told me what to say
She says she loves you
And you know that can't be bad
Yes, she loves you
And you know you should be glad.

Verse 2
She said you hurt her so
She almost lost her mind
But now she says she knows
You're not the hurting kind
She says she loves you
And you know that can't be bad
Yes, she loves you
And you know you should be glad.

Chorus
She loves you, yeah, yeah, yeah
She loves you, yeah, yeah, yeah
With a love like that
You know you should be glad.

Verse 3
You know it's up to you
I think it's only fair
Pride can hurt you too
Apologise to her
Because she loves you
And you know that can't be bad
Yes, she loves you
And you know you should be glad.

Chorus
She loves you, yeah, yeah, yeah
She loves you, yeah, yeah, yeah
With a love like that
You know you should be glad
With a love like that
You know you should be glad
With a love like that
You know you should be glad
Yeah, yeah, yeah
Yeah, yeah, yeah, yeah.

I SHOT THE SHERIFF

Chorus
I shot the sheriff
But I did not shoot the deputy.
I shot the sheriff
But I did not shoot the deputy.

Verse 1
All around in my hometown
They're trying to track me down
They say they want to bring me in
guilty
For the killing of a deputy
For the life of a deputy, but I say...

Chorus 1
I shot the sheriff
But I swear it was in self-defence.
I shot the sheriff
And they say it was a capital offence.

Verse 2
Sheriff John Brown always hated me
For what, I don't know
And every time that I plant a seed
He said kill it before it grows
He said kill it before it grows, I say...

Chorus 2
I shot the sheriff
But I swear it was in self-defence.
I shot the sheriff
But I swear it was in self-defence.

Verse 3
Freedom came my way one day
And I started out of town, yeah
All of a sudden I see Sheriff John
Brown
Aiming to shoot me down
So I shot, I shot him down, but I say...

Chorus 3
I shot the sheriff
But I did not shoot the deputy.
I shot the sheriff
But I did not shoot the deputy.

Verse 4
Reflexes got the better of me
And what is to be must be
Every day the bucket goes to the well
But one day the bottom will drop out
Yes, one day the bottom will drop out
But I say...

Chorus 4
I shot the sheriff
But I did not shoot the deputy.
I shot the sheriff
But I did not shoot no deputy.

SUNNY AFTERNOON

Verse 1
The tax man's taken all my dough
And left me in my stately home
Lazing on a sunny afternoon
And I can't sail my yacht
He's taken everything I've got
All I've got's this sunny afternoon.

Chorus
Save me, save me, save me from
this squeeze
I got a big fat mama trying to
break me.
And I love to live so pleasantly
Live this life of luxury
Lazing on a sunny afternoon.
In the summertime
In the summertime
In the summertime.

Verse 2
My girlfriend's run off with my car
And gone back to her ma and pa
Telling tales of drunkenness and
cruelty.
Now I'm sitting here
Sipping at my ice cold beer
Lazing on a sunny afternoon.

Chorus 2
Help me, help me, help me sail away
Well give me two good reasons
Why I oughta stay.
'Cause I love to live so pleasantly
Live this life of luxury
Lazing on a sunny afternoon.
In the summertime
In the summertime
In the summertime.

Chorus 3
Save me, save me, save me from
this squeeze
I got a big fat mama trying to
break me.
And I love to live so pleasantly
Live this life of luxury
Lazing on a sunny afternoon.
In the summertime
In the summertime
In the summertime
In the summertime
In the summertime.

THERE SHE GOES

Verse 1
There she goes
There she goes again
Racing through my brain
And I just can't contain
This feeling that remains.

Verse 2
There she goes
There she goes again
Pulsing through my vein
And I just can't contain
This feeling that remains.

Bridge
There she goes
There she goes again
She calls my name, pulls my train
No-one else could heal my pain.
But I just can't contain
This feeling that remains.

Verse 3
There she goes
There she goes again
Chasing down my lanes
And I just can't contain
This feeling that remains.

Coda
There she goes
There she goes
There she goes.

HEY JOE

Verse 1
Hey Joe, where you goin' with that gun in your hand?
Hey Joe, I said where you goin' with that gun in your hand?
I'm going out to shoot my old lady
You know I caught her messin' round with another man.
I'm going down to shoot my old lady
You know I caught her messin' round with another man.
(And that ain't too cool.)

Verse 2
Hey Joe, I heard you shot your woman down, you shot her down now.
Hey Joe, I heard you shot your lady down, shot her down to the ground.
Yes, I did, I shot her
You know I caught her messin' round, messin' round town.
I did, I shot her, you know I caught my old lady messin' around town.
And I gave her the gun, I shot her!

Guitar solo

Verse 3
Hey Joe, where you gonna run to now?
Hey Joe, where you gonna run to now (where you gonna go)?
Well, I'm going way down south
Way down to Mexico Way, alright!
Well, I'm going way down south
Way down where I can be free
Ain't no hang man gonna
He ain't gonna put a rope around me.
(You'd better believe, right now.)
Hey Joe, you'd better run now.

ALL RIGHT NOW

Verse 1
There she stood, in the street
Smiling from her head to her feet.
I said 'Hey, what is this?'
Now baby maybe
Maybe she's in need of a kiss?
I said 'Hey, what's your name baby?
Maybe we can see things the same'.
Now don't you wait, or hesitate
Let's move before they raise the parking rate. Ow!

Chorus
All right now, baby it's all right now.
All right now, baby it's all right now.

Verse 2
I took her home to my place
Watching every move on her face.
She said 'Look, what's your game?
Are you tryin' to put me in shame?'
I said 'Slow! Don't go so fast
Don't you think that love can last?'
She said 'Love? Lord above!
Now you're tryin' to trick me in love.'

Chorus
All right now, baby it's all right now.
All right now, baby it's all right now.

Instrumental

Repeat Verse 2

Repeat Chorus to fade

NIGHTS IN WHITE SATIN

Verse 1
Nights in white satin
Never reaching the end
Letters I've written
Never meaning to send.
Beauty I'd always missed
With these eyes before
Just what the truth is
I can't say anymore.

Chorus
'Cause I love you
Yes I love you
Oh, how I love you.

Verse 2
Gazing at people
Some hand in hand
Just what I'm doing
They can't understand.
Some try to tell me
Thoughts they cannot defend
Just what you want to be
You'll be in the end.

Chorus
And I love you
Yes I love you
Oh, how I love you.

Repeat Verse 1

Repeat Chorus x 2

WHILE MY GUITAR GENTLY WEEPS

Verse 1
I look at you all, see the love there that's sleeping
While my guitar gently weeps.
I look at the floor and I see it needs sweeping
Still my guitar gently weeps.

Bridge 1
I don't know why nobody told you
How to unfold your love
I don't know how someone controlled you
They bought and sold you.

Verse 2
I look at the world and I notice it's turning
While my guitar gently weeps.
With every mistake we must surely be learning
Still my guitar gently weeps.

Guitar solo

Bridge 2
I don't know how, you were diverted
You were perverted too.
I don't know how you were inverted
No one alerted you.

Verse 3
I look at you all, see the love there that's sleeping
While my guitar gently weeps.
I look at you all...
Still my guitar gently weeps.

PINBALL WIZARD

Verse 1
Ever since I was a young boy
I played the silver ball
From Soho down to Brighton
I must have played 'em all.
But I ain't seen nothin' like him
In any amusement hall
That deaf, dumb, and blind kid
Sure plays a mean pinball.

Verse 1
He stands like a statue
Becomes part of the machine
Feelin' all the bumpers
Always playin' clean.
Plays by intuitition
The digit counters fall
That deaf, dumb and blind kid
Sure plays a mean pinball.

Chorus
He's a pinball wizard
There has to be a twist
A pinball wizard
Got such a supple wrist.
How do you think he does it?
(I don't know)
What makes him so good?

Verse 3
Ain't got no distractions
Can't hear no buzzes and bells
Don't see no lights a-flashin'
Plays by sense of smell.
Always gets a replay
Never see him fall
That deaf, dumb and blind kid
Sure plays a mean pinball.

Bridge
I thought I was the body table king
But I just handed my pinball crown to him.

Instrumental

Verse 4
He's been on my fav'rite table
He can beat my best
His disciples lead him in
And he just does the rest.
He's got crazy flippin' fingers
Never see him fall
That deaf, dumb and blind kid
Sure plays a mean pinball.

LIGHT MY FIRE

Verse 1
You know that it would be untrue
You know that I would be a liar
If I was to say to you
Girl, we couldn't get much higher.

Chorus
Come on baby, light my fire
Come on baby, light my fire
Try to set the night on fire.

Verse 2
The time to hesitate is through
No time to wallow in the myre
Try now, we can only lose
And our love become a funeral pyre.

Chorus
Come on baby, light my fire
Come on baby, light my fire
Try to set the night on fire.

Instrumental

Repeat Verse 2

Repeat Chorus

Repeat Verse 1

Repeat Chorus

1 **Tuning Notes**

2 **Blue Suede Shoes** (Perkins)
Carlin Music Corporation

3 **Blue Suede Shoes** Backing track only

4 **Driftwood** (Healy)
Sony / ATV Music Publishing (UK) Limited

5 **Driftwood** Backing track only

6 **Sail Away** (Gray)
Chrysalis Music Limited

7 **Sail Away** Backing track only

8 **Wild Wood** (Weller)
Notting Hill Music (UK) Limited

9 **Wild Wood** Backing track only

10 **Roll With It** (Gallagher)
Sony / ATV Music Publishing (UK) Limited

11 **Roll With It** Backing track only

12 **20th Century Boy** (Bolan)
Wizard (Bahamas) Limited

13 **20th Century Boy** Backing track only

14 **She Loves You** (Lennon / McCartney)
Northern Songs / Sony / ATV Music Publishing (UK) Limited

15 **She Loves You** Backing track only

16 **I Shot The Sheriff** (Marley)
Blue Mountain Music Limited

17 **I Shot The Sheriff** Backing track only

18 **Sunny Afternoon** (Davies)
Carlin Music Corporation

19 **Sunny Afternoon** Backing track only

20 **There She Goes** (Mavers)
Universal / Island Music Limited

21 **There She Goes** Backing track only

22 **Hey Joe** (Roberts)
Carlin Music Corporation

23 **Hey Joe** Backing track only

24 **All Right Now** (Rodgers / Fraser)
Blue Mountain Music Limited

25 **All Right Now** Backing track only

26 **Nights In White Satin** (Hayward)
Tyler Music Limited

27 **Nights In White Satin** Backing track only

28 **While My Guitar Gently Weeps** (Harrison)
Harrisongs Limited

29 **While My Guitar Gently Weeps** Backing track only

30 **Pinball Wizard** (Townshend)
Fabulous Music Limited

31 **Pinball Wizard** Backing track only

32 **Light My Fire**
(Morrison / Krieger / Manzarek / Densmore)
Rondor Music (London) Limited

33 **Light My Fire** Backing track only